VOCABULARY
BUILDERS:
BOOK 1

COLLINS
COBUILD

VOCABULARY BUILDERS: BOOK 1

Jim Lawley

THE UNIVERSITY OF BIRMINGHAM

COLLINS COBUILD

HarperCollins*Publishers*

HarperCollins Publishers
77-85 Fulham Palace Road
London   W6 8JB

COBUILD is a trademark of William Collins Sons & Co Ltd

Compilation and Introduction © Jim Lawley 1996
Text © HarperCollins Publishers Ltd 1996

First Published 1996

2 4 6 8 10 9 7 5 3 1

ISBN 0 00 375050 7

Corpus Acknowledgements

We would like to acknowledge the assistance of the many hundreds of
individuals and companies who have kindly given permission for
copyright material to be used in The Bank of English. The written
sources include many national and regional newspapers in Britain and
overseas; magazine and periodical publishers; and book publishers in
Britain, the United States, and Australia. Extensive spoken data has
been provided by radio and television broadcasting companies; research
workers at many universities and other institutions; and numerous
individual contributors. We are grateful to them all.

Note

Entered words that we have reason to believe constitute trademarks
have been designated as such. However, neither the presence nor absence
of such designation should be regarded as affecting the
legal status of any trademark.

Computer typeset by Tradespools Ltd, Frome, Somerset.

Printed and bound in Great Britain by
Caledonian International Book Manufacturing Ltd, Glasgow, G64.

Foreword

This series of COBUILD *Vocabulary Builders* is intended to help learners improve their knowledge of the most frequent words in English. The exercises are derived from the definitions and examples in the *Collins COBUILD English Dictionary*, but the author, Jim Lawley, has reworked the material in a novel and appealing way. We are all familiar with dictionaries as reference books, but they can be so much more than that; here the material from the dictionary is used for the active learning of key vocabulary items. By working out the missing words in the definitions for themselves, and by checking their answers later, students will find it easier to remember not just the meaning of a word but also how it is typically used.

It is well known that COBUILD publications use only real examples; here, new examples from The Bank of English have been added to those from the dictionary in order to increase the information available to the user.

The idea behind the books is based partly on recent pedagogical theory, although the author's implementation of the theory in this way is new. I hope that people using these books will enjoy learning from them. Please write or e-mail me with any comments or suggestions about how to improve these, or any other COBUILD publications.

Gwyneth Fox (Editorial Director)
COBUILD
University of Birmingham Research Park
Vincent Drive
Birmingham B15 2SQ

e-mail: editors@cobuild.collins.co.uk

The COBUILD Series

Founding Editor-in-Chief John Sinclair

Editorial Director Gwyneth Fox

Editorial Team

Editor	John Williams	*Editorial Assistance*	Michael Lax
			Deborah Orpin
Computer Staff	Jeremy Clear	*Secretarial Staff*	Sue Crawley
	Zoe James		Michelle Devereux
	Tim Lane		

Introduction

This book is one of a series of four books which will help you to understand and use the 700 or so most frequent words in the English language. These words are very, very important because they account for nearly 70 per cent of everything that is said and written in English. Some of them combine into phrases (e.g. 'of course' and 'no longer') and phrasal verbs (e.g. 'get up' and 'bring on'), most of them have more than one meaning, and all of them are used by native speakers every day – again and again. Being good at English means being good at using these words. In the *Collins COBUILD English Dictionary* these words appear with five black diamonds (♦♦♦♦♦) to show how important they are. In this book, you will find them listed on pages 111–115. By the time you have worked through these four books you will understand these 'five-diamond' words much better and you should be able to use them correctly and naturally whenever you need to.

How to use this book

There are 55 units in this book. Each unit takes up two facing pages, and is divided into eight separate items indicated by the letters A to H. Each unit is concerned with a particular topic, e.g. 'Talking about People', 'Everyday Situations', 'Body and Health', and each of the items looks at a different five-diamond word connected with that topic.

To see how each item works, look at this example, which focuses on the word 'know'. The following text is taken from the first (left-hand) page of the unit:

> **A**   *She'd known her husband for four years before their wedding.*
> *We all know each other quite well.*
>
> If you **know** someone, you are familiar with them because you have _____ them and talked to them before.

Here, then, you see two examples of the verb 'know' in use and then a definition of the verb 'know' without one of its words. The place where the missing word goes is indicated by an underlined space (_____). The rest of the page consists of another seven words treated in the same way – that is, examples of each word in use followed by its definition from which one word is missing.

The second (right-hand) page of the unit treats the same eight words in a slightly different way. In the case of the verb 'know', for example, on the second page you find:

> **A**   If you _____ someone, you are familiar with them because you have met them and talked to them before.
>
> *He doesn't _____ anybody in New York.*

On the second page, then, it is the word being defined (in this case 'know') which is omitted from the definition and the example (or examples – sometimes there is more than one). So, using this book is easy:

- The words which are missing on the first page of the unit can be found on the second page; the words which are missing on the second page can be found on the first page.

- You simply fill in the eight gaps on the first page; then check your answers by looking at the second page.

- Later, you fill in the gaps on the second page and check your answers by looking at the first page.

In fact, we suggest you study each unit in four stages:

(1) Look at the first page of the unit. Remember that the main aim of this page is to test your *understanding* of the eight words. Read the examples and the definition of each word and try to decide what the word missing from each definition is. If you can't think of the answer straight away, you can try and find it in the lists on pages 111–117. Next, check your answers by looking at the definitions of the words on the second page of the unit. (The definitions appear in a different order on the second page so that you do not see the answer by accident before you want to.) In the case of 'know' above, for example, the missing word is 'met'. The missing word is often also a five-diamond word, and is usually, too, the only word which sounds completely natural in this context. If this is the word you thought of – excellent. If you have thought of a different word which means the same (or nearly the same) as the word given on the second page of the unit, then at least you can feel satisfied that you have understood the definition. However, there will usually be good reasons why the word you have chosen is not quite the best answer. For instance, in the following item:

> **A** *We need to do something about the safety of our children.*
>
> If you do something **about** a problem, you take action in order to try and _____ it.

you might want to fill the space with a verb such as 'stop' or 'prevent'. Either of these would produce a perfectly grammatical English sentence, and the resulting definition would come very close to the actual meaning of 'about'. However, the English verb that is most typically used when you are talking about stopping or preventing problems is 'solve', and this is the word you will find in the corresponding definition on the right-hand page.

> **A** If you do something _____ a problem, you take action in order to try and solve it.
>
> *Even when we knew it was wrong we still did nothing* _____ *it.*

So, your English will improve even more if, in time, you can succeed in giving the same answer as the book – that is, the word on the second page.

In some left-hand page definitions, you will find two (or occasionally more) spaces:

D

I pointed at the boy sitting nearest me.
He pointed to a chair, signalling for her to sit.

If you **point** at someone, you hold out your _____ towards them in order to show someone else where they are. If you **point** at something, you hold out your _____ towards it to make someone notice it.

E

I woke up in the middle of the night.
It was now the middle of November.

The **middle** of an event or period of time is the part that comes _____ the first part and _____ the last part.

Sometimes, it is the same word which fits both spaces; in other cases two different words are required, usually two words that are closely related to each other. It should not be too difficult for you to decide whether you have to put the same word or different words in the two spaces. For instance, in item D above you need the word 'finger' for both spaces, and in item E you need 'after' for the first space and 'before' for the second.

(2) A day or two later, study the second page of the unit. This page tests your ability to *produce* the eight words or phrases highlighted on the first page. Remember: since they are treated in a different order on this page, you can be sure that it's not the position of the definition on the page which will suggest the answer. Read the definitions and examples and try to decide which is the word (or phrase) which is missing from each definition and its following example (or examples). Check your answer by looking back at the definition on the first page of the unit. For example, in the first item we looked at at the beginning of this Introduction:

A

If you _____ someone, you are familiar with them because you have met them and talked to them before.

He doesn't _____ anybody in New York.

the word missing from the definition and the example is, of course, 'know' – the word you can find in the definition on the previous page.

As with the items on the left-hand page, there is usually only one common word which fills the gap satisfactorily. Take a look at the following definitions and examples:

In item B, the word you will find on the left-hand page is 'go'. Although
'turn' means the same as 'go' in this context, and also sounds natural, the
fact that it is already included in the definition tells you that it is not the
answer required. In item F, the only word thats sounds completely natural
is 'small' – and that is the word you will find on the previous page. Although
'little' means almost the same, the phrase 'a little amount of' sounds
unnatural.

Note that, in the right-hand page definitions and examples, a single
underlined space often represents two or more words which are used
together, or a whole phrase (whereas on the left-hand page, it is always a
single word). In a few instances, you will find more than one space in a
right-hand page definition or example, as in the following item:

The reason there are so many spaces in this item is that you are being asked
to supply the phrasal verb 'clear away', and the two parts of the verb can be
separated from each other in the sentence. The only way to show this is to
have separate spaces for 'clear' and 'away'.

(3) The examples of the words on both the left- and the right-hand pages
have been chosen from among hundreds and hundreds of instances of each
five-diamond word taken from books, newspapers, magazines, radio
programmes, and everyday conversations. The examples chosen show
typical grammatical patterns, typical vocabulary, and typical contexts. So
the time spent studying them will be time well-spent. Here are some
suggestions which may help you focus on the way these words are used:

- Read the examples out loud, perhaps trying to say them in the way you
  imagine they may have been originally said.

- Look up the meaning of any unfamiliar words in the examples, in a COBUILD dictionary.

- Translate some of the examples into your language. Then wait a day or so before trying to translate them back into English.

(4) Make a note of the days when you have studied the unit and the words you have found difficult. After a while return to the unit and study it again. The more often you return to the unit, the easier you will find it. Good luck!

Jim Lawley
Ávila 1996

For Christopher

Communication: 1

A

I have just met the man I want to spend the rest of my life with.
We met by chance.

If you **meet** someone, you happen to be in the same place as them and start _____ to them. You may know the other person, but be surprised to see them, or you may not know them at all.

B

Please read the full competition rules on page 179 before entering.
The numbers she put on the chart were 98.4, 64, and 105.

If there is something **on** a piece of _____ , it has been written or printed there.

C

He speaks with a lisp.
I rang the hotel and spoke to Louie.
She cried when she spoke of Oliver.

When you **speak**, you use your voice in order to _____ something.

D

The book is clear, readable and adequately illustrated.
The space telescope has taken the clearest pictures ever of Pluto.

Something that is **clear** is _____ to understand, see, or hear.

E

In the evening I returned to tell Phyllis our relationship was over.
I called Andie to tell her how spectacular the stuff looked.
Her voice breaking with emotion, she told him: 'It doesn't seem fair.'

If you **tell** someone something, you give them _____ .

F

The words of the young woman doctor echoed in his ears.
He looked exhausted and sounded like he was reading someone else's words.

Someone's **words** are what they say or _____ .

G

Rachel already knows as many words in German as she does in English.
Her new classmates knew no Latin.

If you **know** a language, you have _____ it and can understand it.

H

Stella knew what he meant by 'start again'.

If you say what someone _____ **by** a particular word or expression, you are saying what they intend the word or expression to refer to.

Communication: 1

D Something that is _____ is easy to understand, see, or hear.

He repeated his answer, this time in a _____, firm tone of voice.

G If you _____ a language, you have learnt it and can understand it.

It helps to _____ French and Creole if you want to understand some of the lyrics.

E If you _____ someone something, you give them information.

Claire had made me promise to _____ her the truth.
___ _____ us about your moment on the summit.

A If you _____ someone, you happen to be in the same place as them and start talking to them. You may know the other person, but be surprised to see them, or you may not know them at all.

I never believed I would _____ such a charming and sophisticated man.

C When you _____, you use your voice in order to say something.

He tried to _____, but for once, his voice had left him.
She says she must _____ with you at once.

H If you say what someone means _____ a particular word or expression, you are saying what they intend the word or expression to refer to.

'You're unbelievably lucky'—'What do you mean _____ that?'

B If there is something _____ a piece of paper, it has been written or printed there.

How does a poem change when you read it out loud as opposed to it being _____ the page?

F Someone's _____ are what they say or write.

Allied military leaders have said they want actions, not _____ .

2

Everyday Situations: 1

A

They have to get up early in the morning.

When you **get up**, you get out of _____ .

B

You can't see colours at night.
I saw a man making his way towards me.
She can see, hear, touch, smell, and taste.

When you **see** something, you notice it using your _____ .

C

A cup of black tea or black coffee contains no calories.

Black coffee or tea has no _____ or cream added to it.

D

A lot of the money that you pay at the cinema goes back to the film distributors.
Players should be allowed to earn money from advertising.

Money is the coins or bank notes that you use to _____ things, or the sum that you have in a bank account.

E

I keep forgetting it's December.
I turned back after a while, but he kept walking.

If you **keep** doing something, you do it repeatedly or _____ to do it. If someone or something **keeps** you doing something, they cause you to do it repeatedly or to _____ to do it.

F

I lost my keys.
I had to go back for my checkup; they'd lost my X-rays.

If you **lose** something, you do not _____ where it is, for example because you have forgotten where you put it.

G

The shower is easy to install.
It's easy to get a seat at the best shows in town.

If a job or action is **easy**, you can do it without difficulty or effort, because it is not complicated and causes no _____ .

H

Mama made him clean up the plate.
All non-payers of poll tax will be traced and made to pay.

If you **make** someone do something, you _____ them to do it.

Everyday Situations: 1

D   _____ _____ is the coins or bank notes that you use to buy things, or the sum that you have in a bank account.

She probably had more _____ but she didn't spend it.
... discounts and _____ saving offers.

G   If a job or action is _____ , you can do it without difficulty or effort, because it is not complicated and causes no problems.

This is not an _____ task.
The home is situated within _____ access of shops and other facilities.

E   If you _____ doing something, you do it repeatedly or continue to do it. If someone or something _____ you doing something, they cause you to do it repeatedly or to continue to do it.

I will let you have my answer tomorrow. I won't _____ you waiting.

A   When you _____ , you get out of bed.

He used to _____ about seven, have some toast and coffee and then sit down to read the papers.

C   _____ coffee or tea has no milk or cream added.

I drink coffee _____ .

H   If you _____ someone do something, you force them to do it.

You can't _____ me do anything.

B   When you _____ something, you notice it using your eyes.

One could _____ that the dress had been carefully starched.
Did you _____ what happened?

F   If you _____ something, you do not know where it is, for example because you have forgotten where you put it.

Bess didn't _____ the compass. Ned saw Paula take it out of Bess's pocket.

Grammar Words: 1

A

A waiter came and hovered. John caught my look and we both got up and, ignoring the waiter, made our way to the buffet.

You use **the** at the beginning of noun groups to refer to someone or something that you have _____ mentioned or identified.

B

People who can't afford to go to the theatre or concerts can afford to go to football matches.
We cannot buy food, clothes and pay for rent and utilities on $20 a week.

You use **cannot** to indicate that someone is not _____ to do something because circumstances make it impossible for them to do it.

C

I invited him back to my flat for a coffee.
John's my best friend.

A speaker or writer uses **my** to indicate that something _____ or relates to himself or herself.

D

The problem and the answer are very simple.
It is very, very strong evidence indeed.
I'm very sorry.

Very is used to give _____ to an adjective or adverb.

E

I waved goodbye and went down the stone harbour steps.

You use **and** to link two statements about events when one of the events _____ the other.

F

I have never lost the weight I put on in my teens.
Never had he been so free of worry.
That was a mistake. We'll never do it again.

Never means at _____ time in the past or at _____ time in the future.

G

He could never quite remember all our names.
He lives in Rapid City, South Dakota.

You use **he** to refer to a _____ , boy, or male animal.

H

Little traffic was to be seen on the streets.

You can say that something is **to be** seen, heard, or found in a particular place to mean that people _____ see it, hear it, or find it in that place.

Grammar Words: 1

D   _____ ___ is used to give emphasis to an adjective or adverb.

They are getting the hang of it _____ quickly.
Thank you _____ much.
The men were _____ much like my father.

G   You use _____ to refer to a man, boy, or male animal.

Rex did all sorts of tricks. I cried when _____ died.

E   You use _____ to link two statements about events when one of the events follows the other.

He asked for ice for his whiskey _____ proceeded to get drunk.

A   You use _____ at the beginning of noun groups to refer to someone or something that you have already mentioned or identified.

Six of _____ 38 people were Soviet citizens.

C   A speaker or writer uses _____ to indicate that something belongs or relates to himself or herself.

I received a bill for the car rental from _____ credit card company.
_____ understanding was that we'd meet at her place.

H   You can say that something is _____ seen, heard, or found in a particular place to mean that people can see it, hear it, or find it in that place.

They are _____ found all over the world.

B   You use _____ to indicate that someone is not able to do something because circumstances make it impossible for them to do it.

She _____ sleep and the pain is often so bad she wants to scream.

F   _____ means at no time in the past or at no time in the future.

_____ say that. _____ , do you hear?
He was _____ really healthy.
This is _____ to happen again.

Essential Words: 1

A

I started to follow him up the stairs.
It was 1956 when Susanna started the work on the garden.
She started cleaning the kitchen.

If you **start** to do something, you do something that you were not doing before and you _____ doing it.

B

Pat refused to give her any information about Sarah.
Each centre would provide information on technology and training.
For further information contact the number below.

Information about someone or something consists of _____ about them.

C

I don't like myself without a beard.
She wore a brown shirt pressed without a wrinkle.

You use **without** to indicate that someone or something does not _____ or use the thing mentioned.

D

The Pike lives mainly in large rivers and lakes.
In the largest room about a dozen children and seven adults are sitting on the carpet.

A **large** thing or person is greater in _____ than usual or average.

E

Nora thought he was seventeen years old.
The storm is thought to be responsible for as many as four deaths.

If you say that you **think** that something is true or will happen, you mean that you have the impression that it is true or will happen, although you are not _____ of the facts.

F

I like your interpretation better than the one I was taught.
I'd like nothing better than to join you girls.

If you like one thing **better** than another, you like it _____ .

G

The boys were getting bored.
There's no point in getting upset.

You use **get** with adjectives to mean '_____'. For example, if someone **gets cold**, they _____ cold, and if they **get angry**, they _____ angry.

H

The £5 banknote was first issued at the end of the 18th century.
The report is expected by the end of the year.

The **end** of something such as a period of time, an event, a book, or a film is the _____ part of it or the final point in it.

Essential Words: 1

D A _____ _____ thing or person is greater in size than usual or average.

He was a _____ man with a thick square head.

G You use _____ with adjectives to mean 'become'. For example, if someone _____ cold, they become cold, and if they _____ angry, they become angry.

From here on, it can only _____ _____ better.

E If you say that you _____ that something is true or will happen, you mean that you have the impression that it is true or will happen, although you are not certain of the facts.

She's in Napa, I _____ .
'Did Mr Stevens ever mention her to you?'—'No, I don't _____ so.'

A If you _____ to do something, you do something that you were not doing before and you continue doing it.

I decided to _____ trying to write.

C You use _____ to indicate that someone or something does not have or use the thing mentioned.

... a meal _____ barbecue sauce.

H The _____ of something such as a period of time, an event, a book, or a film is the last part of it or the final point in it.

You will have the chance to ask questions at the _____ .

B _____ about someone or something consists of facts about them.

... an important piece of _____ .
The _____ was passed on to another government department.

F If you like one thing _____ than another, you like it more.

They liked it _____ when it rained.

Society: 1

A
This reflects attitudes and values prevailing in society.

Society is _____ in general, thought of as a large organized group.

B
... the leader of Poland's Solidarity movement, Mr Lech Walesa.

The **leader** of a group of people or an organization is the person who is _____ control of it or _____ charge of it.

C
He joined the Army five years ago.

If you **join** an organization, you become a _____ of it or start work as an employee of it.

D
Indonesia is the fifth most populous country in the world.
... that disputed boundary between the two countries.

A **country** is one of the political units which the _____ is divided into, covering a particular area of land.

E
The children are not allowed to watch violent TV programmes.
The Government will allow them to advertise on radio and television.
They will be allowed home.

If someone **is allowed** to do something, it is all right for them to do it and they will not _____ into trouble.

F
She interviewed six women who have reached positions of great power and influence.
In a democracy, power must be divided.

If someone has **power**, they have a lot of _____ over people and activities.

G
Mother Teresa is an elderly nun who has devoted her life to fighting poverty.
I've spent a lifetime fighting against racism and prejudice.

If you **fight** something unpleasant, you _____ in a determined way to prevent it or stop it happening.

H
... the evolution of British foreign policy under Thatcher.
... the UN's policy-making body.

A **policy** is a set of ideas or plans that is used as a basis for making decisions, especially in _____ , economics, or business.

9

Society: 1

D A _____ is one of the political units which the world is divided into, covering a particular area of land.

Young people do move around the _____ quite a bit these days.

G If you _____ something unpleasant, you try in a determined way to prevent it or stop it happening.

More units to _____ forest fires are planned.
... the _____ against drug addiction.

E If someone _____ to do something, it is all right for them to do it and they will not get into trouble.

A civil administration official said that no employee _____ to give out information without permission.

A _____ is people in general, thought of as a large organized group.

... the role of intellectuals in modern _____ .

C If you _____ an organization, you become a member of it or start work as an employee of it.

She _____ a dance company which took her around the world.

H A _____ is a set of ideas or plans that is used as a basis for making decisions, especially in politics, economics, or business.

Mr. O'Malley attacked the new government's economic _____ .

B The _____ of a group of people or an organization is the person who is in control of it or in charge of it.

The Republican Party's _____ , Mr Franz Schoenhuber, has resigned.

F If someone has _____ , they have a lot of control over people and activities.

... a _____ struggle at the top of Albania's ruling Communist Party.

Talking about People: 1

A

Gifford was a friend. I'd known him for nine years.
Do you two know each other?

If you **know** someone, you are familiar with them because you have
_____ them and talked to them before.

B

I had a long talk about this with my best friend.
She never was a close friend of mine.

A **friend** is someone who you know well and _____ , but who is
not related to you.

C

You have a good mind.
Studying stretched my mind and got me thinking about things.

Your **mind** is your ability to _____ and reason.

D

I would be insanely jealous if Bill left me for another woman.

If you **leave** your husband, wife, or some other person with whom
you have had a close relationship, you _____ living with them
or you finish the relationship.

E

If we agreed all the time it would be a bit boring, wouldn't it?
So we both agree there's a problem?
I see your point but I'm not sure I agree with you.

If people **agree** with each other about something, they have the
_____ opinion about it or say that they have the _____
opinion.

F

I am feeling very depressed.
I remember feeling sick.
Suddenly I felt a sharp pain in my shoulder.
I felt as if all my strength had gone.

If you **feel** a particular emotion or physical sensation, you experience
it in your mind or your _____ .

G

She is in a bit of a bad mood because she's just given up smoking.

If you are in a **bad** mood, you are cross and behave unpleasantly to
_____ .

H

Millions of people have lost their homes.
... the people of Angola.
It is illegal and could endanger other people's lives.

People are men, women, and _____ . **People** is normally used
as the plural of 'person', instead of 'persons'.

Talking about People: 1

D
If you _ _____ your husband, wife, or some other person with whom you have had a close relationship, you stop living with them or you finish the relationship.

Frank clearly never intended to _____ his wife or destroy their marriage.

G
If you are in a _____ mood, you are cross and behave unpleasantly to people.

I annoyed everybody in the morning 'cos I was in a _____ mood.

E
If people _____ with each other about something, they have the same opinion about it or say that they have the same opinion.

I _____ with you about the gun situation.
I _____ with you that the open system is by far the best.
'It's appalling.'—'It is. I _____ .'

A
If you _____ someone, you are familiar with them because you have met them and talked to them before.

He doesn't _____ anybody in London.

C
Your _____ is your ability to think and reason.

... an excellent training for the young _____ .

H
_____ are men, women, and children. _____ is normally used as the plural of 'person', instead of 'persons'.

... homeless young _____ .
I don't think _____ should make promises they don't mean to keep.

B
A _____ is someone who you know well and like, but who is not related to you.

... Sara's old _____ , Ogden.

F
If you _____ a particular emotion or physical sensation, you experience it in your mind or your body.

I will always _____ grateful to that little guy.
You won't _____ a thing.

Talking about Things: 1

A

'What's that thing in the middle of the fountain?'—'Some kind of statue, I guess.'
She was in the middle of clearing the breakfast things.
A strange thing happened.

You can use **thing** to refer to any _____ , feature, or event when you cannot, need not, or do not want to refer to it more precisely.

B

'What colour is the car?'—'Red.'
Her silk dress was sky-blue, the colour of her eyes.

The **colour** of something is the appearance that it has as a result of the way in which it reflects _____ .

C

Australia's a big country.
Her husband was a big man.

A **big** person or thing is _____ in physical size.

D

His name was Hansen, a common name in Norway.
Oil pollution is the commonest cause of death for seabirds.

If something is **common**, it is found in large numbers or it happens

_____ .

E

What was Bulgaria like?
What did she look like?

If you ask or talk about what something or someone is **like**, you are asking or talking about their _____ , their characteristics, or their qualities.

F

Try on clothing and shoes to make sure they fit.

If you **try on** a piece of clothing, you put it on to see if it fits you or if it _____ nice.

G

She was wearing a black coat with a white collar.
He had thick black hair.

Something that is **black** is of the darkest colour that there is, the colour of the sky at night when there is no _____ at all.

H

Her sons are the most important thing in her life.
The planned general strike represents an important economic challenge to the government.
This gold is every bit as important to me as it is to you.

Something that is **important** has _____ significance or value, or is necessary.

13

Talking about Things: 1

D   If something is _____ , it is found in large numbers or it happens often.

Earthquakes are not _____ in this part of the world.
It was _____ practice for prisoners to carve objects from animal bones to pass the time.

G   Something that is _____ is of the darkest colour that there is, the colour of the sky at night when there is no light at all.

He was dressed all in _____ .

E   If you ask or talk about what something or someone is _____ , you are asking or talking about their appearance, their characteristics, or their qualities.

What was it _____ growing up in Hillsborough?
Joe still has no concept of what it's _____ to be the sole parent.

A   You can use _____ to refer to any object, feature, or event when you cannot, need not, or do not want to refer to it more precisely.

If you could change one _____ about yourself, what would it be?

C   A _____ person or thing is large in physical size.

The car was too _____ to fit into our garage.

H   Something that is _____ has great significance or value, or is necessary.

It's _____ to answer her questions as honestly as you can.
It was _____ that he rest.

B   The _____ of something is the appearance that it has as a result of the way in which it reflects light.

Judi's favourite _____ is pink.

F   If you _____ a piece of clothing, you put it on to see if it fits you or if it looks nice.

She let me _____ her wedding dress.

Movement and Travel: 1

A

He moved around the room, putting his possessions together.
She moved away from the window.

When you **move**, you change your position or _____ to a different place.

B

How far is Pawtucket from Providence?
How far is it to Malcy?
You can only judge how high something is when you know how far away it is.

If you ask how **far** a place is, you are asking what distance it is from you or from another place. If you ask how **far** someone went, you are asking what distance they travelled, or what place they _____ .

C

Combine the remaining ingredients and put them into a dish.

If you put one thing **into** another, you put the _____ thing inside the _____ .

D

Inside, a guard directed them to the right.

If you **direct** someone somewhere, you _____ them how to get there.

E

I thought we might go for a drive on Sunday.

A **drive** is a journey in a _____ or other vehicle.

F

His destination was Chobham Common, a long way from his Cotswold home.
The long journey tired him.

A **long** distance is a great distance. A **long** journey or route _____ a great distance.

G

He wanted to visit his brother in Worcester.
He was visited by an old friend from Iraq.

If you **visit** someone, you go to _____ them and spend time with them.

H

He was carrying a briefcase.
He carried the plate through to the dining-room.
She carried her son to the car.

If you **carry** something, you take it with you, _____ it so that it does not touch the ground.

Movement and Travel: 1

D   If you _____ someone somewhere, you tell them how to get there.

Could you _____ them to Dr Lamont's office, please.

G   If you _____ someone, you go to see them and spend time with them.

Bill would _____ on weekends.
Helen had recently paid him a _____ .

E   A _____ is a journey in a car or other vehicle.

He invited me to go for a _____ .

A   When you _____ , you change your position or go to a different place.

She waited for him to get up, but he didn't _____ .
There was so much furniture you could hardly _____ without bumping into something.

C   If you put one thing _____ another, you put the first thing inside the second.

Until the 1980s almost all olives were packed _____ jars by hand.

H   If you _____ something, you take it with you, holding it so that it does not touch the ground.

If your job involves a lot of paperwork, you're going to need something to _____ it all in.

B   If you ask how _____ a place is, you are asking what distance it is from you or from another place. If you ask how _____ someone went, you are asking what distance they travelled, or what place they reached.

How _____ can you throw?
She followed the tracks as _____ as the road.

F   A _____ distance is a great distance. A _____ journey or route covers a great distance.

I went for a _____ walk.

Body and Health: 1

A
Your life is in danger.
The intense fighting is reported to have claimed many lives.

If you refer to someone's **life**, you mean their state of being alive, especially when there is a risk or danger of them _____ .

B
I'm not very well today, I can't come in.

If you are **well**, you are healthy and not _____ .

C
The largest organ in the body is the liver.

Your **body** is all your physical parts, _____ your head, arms, and legs.

D
I opened my eyes and looked.
Maria's eyes filled with tears.

Your **eyes** are the parts of your body with which you _____ .

E
I put my hand into my pocket and pulled out the letter.
Sylvia, camera in hand, asked, 'Where do we go first?'

Your **hands** are the parts of your body at the _____ of your arms. Each hand has four fingers and a thumb.

F
Queen Elizabeth Hospital is a children's hospital with 120 beds.
A couple of weeks later my mother went into hospital.

A **hospital** is a place where people who are ill are looked after by nurses and _____ .

G
Tea contains caffeine. It's bad for your health.

A person's **health** is the condition of their body and the extent to which it is _____ from illness or is able to resist illness.

H
A year later my dog died and I went to pieces.
Sadly, both he and my mother died of cancer.
Reynolds says he is haunted by the ghosts of friends who died young.

When people, animals, and plants **die**, they stop _____ .

Body and Health: 1

D

Your ___ _____ are the parts of your body with which you see.

... a tall, thin white-haired old lady with piercing dark brown _____ .

G

A person's _____ is the condition of their body and the extent to which it is free from illness or is able to resist illness.

My _____ is good, apart from the occasional headache.

E

Your _____ are the parts of your body at the end of your arms. Each _____ has four fingers and a thumb.

He stood with his _____ in the pockets of his long black coat.

A

If you refer to someone's _____ , you mean their state of being alive, especially when there is a risk or danger of them dying.

A nurse began to try to save his _____ .

C

Your _____ is all your physical parts, including your head, arms, and legs.

He stands for a long time gazing at his naked _____ in the mirror.

H

When people, animals, and plants _____ , they stop living.

I would _____ a very happy person if I could stay in music my whole life.

B

If you are _____ , you are healthy and not ill.

I hope you're _____ .

F

A _____ is a place where people who are ill are looked after by nurses and doctors.

He may be able to leave _____ early next week.

Time: 1

A

. . . a two-week period of time.
Time passed, and still Ma did not appear.

Time is what we measure in seconds, _____ , hours, days, and years.

B

I wanted him to come with us today, but he couldn't.

You use **today** to refer to the _____ on which you are speaking or writing.

C

I got married last July.
He never made it home at all last night.

You use **last** in expressions such as 'last Friday' and 'last year' to refer, for example, to the most _____ Friday or year.

D

They often spent Christmas at Prescott Hill.
They used these words freely, often in front of their parents too.

If something **often** happens, it happens _____ times or much of the time.

E

The trial is due to begin next month.
. . . an exhibition which opens this month at London's Design Museum.

A **month** is one of the twelve periods of time that a _____ is divided into, for example January or February.

F

He was killed a few days ago in a skiing accident.
The meeting is the first ever between the two sides since the war there began 14 years ago.

You use **ago** when you are referring to _____ time. For example, if something happened one year **ago**, it is one year since it happened. If it happened a long time **ago**, it is a long time since it happened.

G

The weeks go so quickly!

If you say that a period of time **goes** quickly or slowly, you mean that it seems to _____ quickly or slowly.

H

It was late in the afternoon.
She had to work late at night.
His autobiography was written late in life.

Late means near the _____ of a day, week, year, or other period of time.

Time: 1

D

If something _____ happens, it happens many times or much of the time.

It was _____ hard to work and do the course at the same time.
That doesn't happen very _____ .

G

If you say that a period of time _____ quickly or slowly, you mean that it seems to pass quickly or slowly.

It was lovely to be at Apple St again, the day _____ so quickly.

E

A _____ is one of the twelve periods of time that a year is divided into, for example January or February.

I send him fifteen dollars a _____ .

A

_____ is what we measure in seconds, minutes, hours, days, and years.

As _____ went on the visits got more and more regular.
The social significance of religion has changed over _____ .

C

You use _____ in expressions such as '_____ Friday' and '_____ year' to refer, for example, to the most recent Friday or year.

It is not surprising they did so badly in _____ year's elections.

H

_____ means near the end of a day, week, year, or other period of time.

The case is expected to end _____ next week.
Since _____ last year the border area has been the scene of heavy fighting.

B

You use _____ to refer to the day on which you are speaking or writing.

_____ is Friday, September 14th.

F

You use _____ when you are referring to past time. For example, if something happened one year _____ , it is one year since it happened. If it happened a long time _____ , it is a long time since it happened.

Harry's daughter is dead. She died long _____ .

Everyday Situations: 2

A

He has helped to raise a lot of money.
My mum used to help cook the meals for the children.
America's priority is to help nations defend themselves.
You can of course help by giving them a donation directly.

If you **help** someone, you make it _____ for them to do something, for example by doing part of the work for them or by giving them advice or money.

B

'I like this dress,' she said. 'Keep it. You can have it,' said Daphne.
Lathan had to choose between marrying her and keeping his job.

If you **keep** something, you continue to have it in your possession and do not throw it away, _____ it away, or sell it.

C

Beer cost three pounds a bottle.
A thousand pounds worth of jewellery and silver has been stolen.

The **pound** is the unit of _____ which is used in Britain. It is represented by the symbol £. One British pound is divided into a hundred pence.

D

I sold everything I owned except for my car and my books.
His heir sold the painting to the London art dealer Agnews.

If you **sell** something that you own, you let someone have it in _____ for money.

E

You wash while I make some lunch.

If you **make** a meal or a drink, you _____ it.

F

She could change into a different outfit in two minutes.

When you get **into** a piece of clothing, you _____ it on.

G

He gave her a blank look, as if he had no idea who she was.

If you give someone a particular kind of **look**, you look at them with your expression showing what you are feeling or _____ .

H

I tried to get in touch with you yesterday evening, but I think you were out.
Perhaps I shouldn't say that – I might get into trouble.

If you **get** into a particular state or situation, you cause or allow yourself to _____ in that state or situation.

Everyday Situations: 2

D   If you __ _____ something that you own, you let someone have it in return for money.

I can't _____ the business and I'm going bankrupt.
It's not a very good time to _____ at the moment.

G   If you give someone a particular kind of _____ , you _____ at them with your expression showing what you are feeling or thinking.

Sally spun round, a feigned _____ of surprise on her face.

E   If you _____ a meal or a drink, you prepare it.

Would you like me to _____ us all a coffee?

A   If you _____ someone, you make it easier for them to do something, for example by doing part of the work for them or by giving them advice or money.

I was only trying to _____ .
If you're not willing to _____ me, I'll find somebody who will.

C   The _____ is the unit of money which is used in Britain. It is represented by the symbol £. One British _____ is divided into a hundred pence.

... multi-million _____ profits.
... a _____ coin.

H   If you _____ into a particular state or situation, you cause or allow yourself to be in that state or situation.

How did we _____ into this recession, and what can we do to _____ out of it?

B   If you _____ something, you continue to have it in your possession and do not throw it away, give it away, or sell it.

'I like this dress,' she said. '_____ it. You can have it,' said Daphne.

F   When you get _____ a piece of clothing, you put it on.

He put on his underwear and got _____ his suit.

Things We Say: 1

A

'Who is it?' he called.—'It's your neighbor.'

You use **it** when you are telling someone _____ you are, or asking them _____ they are, especially at the beginning of a phone call. You also use **it** in statements and questions about the identity of other people.

B

Let me take your coat.

You use **let me** when you are _____ politely to do something.

C

I would challenge the, er, suggestion that we're in third place.

Er is used to represent the sound that people make when they hesitate, especially _____ they decide what to say next.

D

You needn't worry.

If you tell someone that they **needn't** do something, or that something **needn't** happen, you are reassuring them that it is not necessary or inevitable, because a situation is not as _____ as they might think.

E

'Can I just say something about the cup game on Saturday?'—'Yes, of course you can.'

You use **of course** as a polite way of giving _____ ; used in spoken English.

F

'Oh!' Kenny blinked. 'Has everyone gone?'
'Oh, my God,' Korontzis moaned.

You use **oh** to express a feeling such as _____ , pain, annoyance, or joy; used mainly in spoken English.

G

Millson regarded her thoughtfully. Perhaps she was right.
In the end they lose millions, perhaps billions.
Perhaps, in time, the message will get through.

You use **perhaps** to express uncertainty, for example, when you do not know that something is definitely true, or when you are mentioning something that may possibly happen in the _____ in the way you describe.

H

I could kill you! I swear I could!
'Welcome back' was all they said. I could have kissed them!

You use **could** when you are expressing strong _____ about something, as if you want to do the thing mentioned, although you do not do it.

Things We Say: 1

D

If you tell someone that they _____ do something, or that something _____ happen, you are reassuring them that it is not necessary or inevitable, because a situation is not as bad as they might think.

This _____ take long, Simon.

G

You use _____ to express uncertainty, for example, when you do not know that something is definitely true, or when you are mentioning something that may possibly happen in the future in the way you describe.

He does not paint for very long on any one painting, _____ for two and a half hours at a time.
It was bulky, _____ three feet long and almost as high.
They'd come soon, _____ when the radio broadcast was over.

E

You use _____ as a polite way of giving permission; used in spoken English.

'Could I see these documents?'—'_____ .'

A

You use _____ when you are telling someone who you are, or asking them who they are, especially at the beginning of a phone call. You also use _____ in statements and questions about the identity of other people.

Hello Freddy, _____ 's only me, Maxine.

C

_____ is used to represent the sound that people make when they hesitate, especially while they decide what to say next.

People that are addicted to drugs get _____ help from the government one way or another.

H

You use _____ when you are expressing strong feelings about something, as if you want to do the thing mentioned, although you do not do it.

She _____ have screamed with tension.

B

You use _____ when you are offering politely to do something.

_____ get you something to drink.

F

You use _____ to express a feeling such as surprise, pain, annoyance, or joy; used mainly in spoken English.

_____ , I'm so glad you're here.

24

Places and Positions: 1

A

It's a beautiful part of the world.
More than anything, I'd like to drive around the world.

The world is the planet that we _____ on.

B

He drew his chair nearer the fire.
He crouched as near to the door as he could.
Where's the nearest telephone?

If something is **near** a place, thing, or person, it is a _____ distance from them.

C

. . . the small town of St Augustine, in north-east Florida.

A **town** is a place with a lot of streets and _____ where people live and work. Towns are larger than villages and smaller than cities.

D

He took the case out of her hand and set it on the floor.

If you **set** something somewhere, you _____ it there, especially in a careful or deliberate way.

E

He is sitting beside her on the sofa.
On the table were dishes piled high with sweets.

If someone or something is **on** a surface or object, the surface or object is immediately below them and is _____ their weight.

F

. . . an international agreement against exporting arms to states that sponsor terrorism.
. . . Kuwait International Airport.

International means between or involving different _____ .

G

In Britain cars drive on the left.
. . . the brick wall to the left of the conservatory.

The **left** is one of two opposite directions, sides, or positions. If you are facing north and you turn to the left, you will be facing _____ . In the word 'to', the 't' is to the left of the 'o'.

H

In the old days the woman stayed at home and the man earned the money.

If you **stay** where you are, you continue to be there and do _____ leave.

Places and Positions: 1

D

If you _____ ____ something somewhere, you put it there, especially in a careful or deliberate way.

When he _____ his glass down he spilled a little drink.

G

The _____ is one of two opposite directions, sides, or positions. If you are facing north and you turn to the _____ , you will be facing west. In the word 'to', the 't' is to the _____ of the 'o'.

Beaufort Castle is on your _____ .
Turn _____ at the crossroads into Clay Lane.

E

If someone or something is _____ a surface or object, the surface or object is immediately below them and is supporting their weight.

The cushions were soft blue to match the Chinese rug _____ the floor.

A

_____ is the planet that we live on.

The satellite enables us to calculate their precise location anywhere in _____ .

C

A _____ is a place with a lot of streets and buildings where people live and work. _____ are larger than villages and smaller than cities.

Parking can be tricky in the _____ centre.

H

If you _____ where you are, you continue to be there and do not leave.

'_____ here,' Trish said. 'I'll bring the car down the drive to take you back.'

B

If something is _____ a place, thing, or person, it is a short distance from them.

Don't come _____ me.
Her children went back every year to stay in a farmhouse _____ the cottage.

F

_____ means between or involving different countries.

The Cuban Government has asked for emergency aid from the _____ community.

Essential Words: 2

A

These diets provide everything your body needs.
I need you to do something for me.

If you **need** something, or **need** to do something, you cannot successfully achieve what you want or live properly _____ it.

B

Do you think they have a chance of beating Australia?
Tim's chances of survival were still slim.

If there is a **chance** of something happening, it is _____ that it will happen.

C

Experts believe that the coming drought will be extensive.
I believe you have something of mine.
We believe them to be hidden here in this apartment.

If you **believe** that something is true, you _____ that it is true; a formal use. You can say **'I believe'** to indicate that you are not completely sure that what you are saying is accurate or to make a statement sound more factual and less emotional.

D

You're very special to me, darling.
There are strong arguments for holidays at Easter and Christmas because these are special occasions.

Someone or something that is **special** is better or more important than _____ people or things.

E

It's a good idea to keep a stock of slimmers' meals for when you're too busy or tired to cook.
I really like the idea of helping people.

An **idea** is a plan, suggestion, or possible course of _____ .

F

In Scotland, young people can marry at 16.
He played with his younger brother.

A **young** person, animal, or plant has not lived or existed for very _____ and is not yet mature.

G

The couple had been dating for almost three years.
Storms have been hitting almost all of Britain recently.
The effect is almost impossible to describe.

You use **almost** to indicate that something is not completely the case but is _____ the case.

H

Economists say this trend is likely to continue throughout the '90s.

If someone or something is **likely** to do something, they will very _____ do it.

Essential Words: 2

D
Someone or something that is _____ is better or more important than other people or things.

Just to see him was something _____ .
My _____ guest will be comedian Ben Elton.

G
You use _____ to indicate that something is not completely the case but is nearly the case.

The arrested man will _____ certainly be kept at this police station.
He contracted Spanish flu, which _____ killed him.

E
An _____ is a plan, suggestion, or possible course of action.

She told me she'd had a brilliant _____ .

A
If you _____ something, or _____ to do something, you cannot successfully achieve what you want or live properly without it.

A baby does not _____ to wear shoes until he starts to walk.
I _____ you here, Wally.

C
If you _____ that something is true, you think that it is true; a formal use. You can say 'I _____ ' to indicate that you are not completely sure that what you are saying is accurate or to make a statement sound more factual and less emotional.

The main problem, I _____ , lies elsewhere.
'You've never heard of him?'—'I don't _____ so.'

H
If someone or something is _____ to do something, they will very probably do it.

Once people have seen that something actually works, they are much more _____ to accept change.

B
If there is a _____ of something happening, it is possible that it will happen.

This partnership has a good _____ of success.
There was really very little _____ that Ben would ever have led a normal life.

F
A _____ person, animal, or plant has not lived or existed for very long and is not yet mature.

You weren't so very _____ when she died; you were old enough to remember.
I crossed the hill, and found myself in a field of _____ barley.

Numbers: 1

A *I seem to remember that Sam told a number of lies.*

If there are a **number** of things or people, there are _____ of them. If there are any **number** of things or people, there is a large quantity of them.

B *... their second child.*
My son just got married for the second time.
... the Second World War.

The **second** item in a series is the one that you count as number _____ .

C *... more than a thousand acres of land.*
... a quarter of an hour.

You use **a** or **an** instead of the number '_____', especially with words of measurement such as 'hundred', 'hour', and 'metre', and with fractions such as 'half', 'quarter', and 'third'.

D *In my local health centre there's about forty parking spaces.*

About is used in front of a number to show that the number is not _____ .

E *The programme was viewed on television in millions of homes.*

If you talk about **millions** of people or things, you mean that there is a very _____ number of them.

F *The airport had been closed for more than a year.*
... classy leather and silk jackets at more than £250.

You use **more than** before a number or an _____ to say that the actual number or _____ is even greater.

G *President Bush will need all his skill in the coming weeks to carry American public opinion with him.*
He was told to pack up all of his letters and personal belongings.

You use **all** to refer to the _____ of a particular group or thing, or to everyone or everything of a particular kind.

H *Astronauts will make a final attempt today to rescue a communications satellite from its useless orbit.*
This is the fifth and probably final day of testimony.

In a series of events, things, or people, the **final** one is the _____ one.

Numbers: 1

D

_____ is used in front of a number to show that the number is not exact.

When I was _____ nine I started to have very vivid dreams.

G

You use _____ to refer to the whole of a particular group or thing, or to everyone or everything of a particular kind.

85 percent of _____ American households owe money on mortgages.
Germany, like _____ great nations, will not change its personality.
He was passionate about _____ literature.
He was talking to _____ of us.

E

If you talk about _____ of people or things, you mean that there is a very large number of them.

This wretched war has brought misery to _____ .

A

If there are a _____ of things or people, there are several of them. If there are any _____ of things or people, there is a large quantity of them.

There must be any _____ of people in my position.

C

You use _____ or _____ instead of the number 'one', especially with words of measurement such as 'hundred', 'hour', and 'metre', and with fractions such as 'half', 'quarter', and 'third'.

The skirts were shortened _____ inch or two.

H

In a series of events, things, or people, the _____ one is the last one.

Hampson sealed victory with a goal from the _____ kick of the game.

B

The _____ item in a series is the one that you count as number two.

She was the _____ of nine children.
... King Charles the _____ .
Britain came _____ in the Prix St Georges Derby.

F

You use _____ before a number or an amount to say that the actual number or amount is even greater.

... a survey of _____ 1,500 schools.

Grammar Words: 2

A
Here, can I really have your jeans when you go?
You cannot ask for your money back before the agreed date.

You use **can** to indicate that someone is _____ to do something. You use **cannot** or **can't** to indicate that someone is not _____ to do something.

B
A waiter entered with a tray bearing a glass and a bottle of whiskey.

You use **a** or **an** when you are referring to someone or something for the _____ time and you cannot assume that your listener or reader knows which particular thing you are talking about.

C
I locked myself out of our apartment and had to break in.

A speaker or writer uses **our** to indicate that something _____ or relates both to himself or herself and to one or more other people.

D
She rested for a while, then had a wash and changed her clothes.
They were having a long wait for someone to serve them.

You can use **have** followed by a noun to talk about an action or event, when it would also be possible to use a verb. For example, you can say 'I had a look at it' instead of 'I _____ at it'.

E
I felt quite bitter about it at the time.
I was doing quite well, but I wasn't earning a lot of money.

You use **quite** to indicate that something is the case to a fairly great extent. **Quite** is _____ emphatic than 'very' and 'extremely'.

F
The fruit inside should be no larger than a currant or a raisin.

You use **no** when saying that something does not exceed a particular amount or number, or does not have _____ of a particular quality than something else.

G
They haven't finished yet.
No decision has yet been made.

You use **yet** in negative statements to indicate that something has not happened up to the present time, although it _____ will happen.

H
Switch to an interest-paying current account and stay in credit. Most banks and larger building societies now offer these accounts.

You use **these** in front of noun groups to refer to someone or something that you have _____ mentioned or identified.

Grammar Words: 2

D You can use _____ followed by a noun to talk about an action or event, when it would also be possible to use a verb. For example, you can say 'I _____ a look at it' instead of 'I looked at it'.

I'll _____ a think about that.

G You use _____ in negative statements to indicate that something has not happened up to the present time, although it probably will happen.

'Has the murderer been caught?'—'Not _____ .'

E You use _____ to indicate that something is the case to a fairly great extent. _____ is less emphatic than 'very' and 'extremely'.

I was _____ a long way away, on the terrace.

A You use _____ to indicate that someone is allowed to do something. You use _____ or _____ to indicate that someone is not allowed to do something.

Anyone _____ join our organization.
I'm on tablets and the doctor's told me I _____ drive.

C A speaker or writer uses _____ to indicate that something belongs or relates both to himself or herself and to one or more other people.

We're expecting _____ first baby.

H You use _____ in front of noun groups to refer to someone or something that you have already mentioned or identified.

A steering committee has been formed. _____ people can make decisions in ten minutes which would usually take us months.

B You use _____ or _____ when you are referring to someone or something for the first time and you cannot assume that your listener or reader knows which particular thing you are talking about.

Today you've got _____ new teacher taking you.

F You use _____ when saying that something does not exceed a particular amount or number, or does not have more of a particular quality than something else.

It is to start broadcasting _____ later than the end of 1994.

Work: 1

A

Weiner works for the US Department of Transport.
I started working in a recording studio.
He worked as a bricklayer's mate.

People who **work** have a job, usually one which they are _____ to do.

B

'What does your father do?'—'Well, he's a civil servant.'

If you ask someone what they **do**, you want to know what their _____ or profession is.

C

He had an office big enough for his desk and chair, plus his VDU.
At about 4.30 p.m. Audrey arrived at the office.

An **office** is a room or a part of a _____ where people work sitting at desks.

D

I knew he worked for a security firm.
Have you had any experience writing for radio?

If you work or do a job **for** someone, you are _____ by them.

E

It's hard to tell what effect this latest move will have.
She found it hard to accept some of the criticisms directed towards her and her work.

Something that is **hard** is very _____ to do or deal with.

F

In the early 1980s, it was easy to get into the rental business.

If you move or go **into** a particular career or business, you start _____ in it.

G

... a commission appointed by the police chief.

The **chief** of an organization is the person who is _____ it.

H

The staff were very good.
The outpatient program has a staff of six people.
Many employers seek diversity in their staffs.

The **staff** of an organization are the _____ who work for it.

Work: 1

D   If you work or do a job _____ someone, you are employed by them.

... a buyer _____ one of the largest chain stores in the south.

G   The _____ of an organization is the person who is in charge of it.

... Gorbachev's _____ of security.

E   Something that is _____ is very difficult to do or deal with.

Our traveller's behaviour on the journey is _____ to explain.
That's a very _____ question.

A   People who _____ have a job, usually one which they are paid to do.

Where do you _____ ?
I want to _____ , I don't want to be on welfare.

C   An _____ is a room or a part of a building where people work sitting at desks.

Telephone their head _____ for more details.
... an _____ block.

H   The _____ of an organization are the people who work for it.

He thanked his _____ .
... members of _____ .

B   If you ask someone what they _____ , you want to know what their job or profession is.

He knew what he wanted to _____ from the age of 14.

F   If you move or go _____ a particular career or business, you start working in it.

He closed down the business and went _____ politics.

Communication: 2

A

I think you heard and also understand me.
Rusty nodded as though she understood the old woman.
He was speaking poor English, trying to make himself understood.

If you **understand** someone or **understand** what they are saying, you know what they _____ .

B

I had received a letter from a very close friend.
... a letter of resignation.

If you write a **letter** to someone, you write a message on paper and _____ it to them, usually by post.

C

'I'm sorry,' he said.
She said they were very impressed.
Forty-one people are said to have been seriously hurt.
Did he say where he was going?

When you **say** something, you speak _____ .

D

Ingredients are listed in order of the amount used.

To **list** several things such as reasons or names means to write or say them one after another, usually in a particular _____ .

E

The longest chapter in almost any book on baby care is on feeding.
They offer a free counselling service which can offer help and advice on legal matters.

Books, discussions, or ideas **on** a particular subject are _____ with that subject.

F

She asked me back to her house.

If you **ask** someone to an event or place, you _____ them to go there.

G

He still travels to London regularly for business meetings.

A **meeting** is an event in which a group of people come _____ to discuss things or make decisions.

H

Is it right for the Church to express a view on political issues?

An **issue** is an important subject that people are arguing _____ or discussing.

Communication: 2

D
To _____ several things such as reasons or names means to write or say them one after another, usually in a particular order.

The pupils were asked to _____ the sports they loved most and hated most.

G
A _____ is an event in which a group of people come together to discuss things or make decisions.

Can we have a _____ to discuss that?

E
Books, discussions, or ideas _____ a particular subject are concerned with that subject.

He declined to give any information _____ the Presidential election.
China's comments _____ the US decision were relatively restrained.

A
If you _____ someone or _____ what they are saying, you know what they mean.

I don't _____ what you are talking about.

C
When you _____ something, you speak words.

I hope you didn't _____ anything about Gretchen.
You didn't _____ much when you telephoned.
It doesn't sound exactly orthodox, if I may _____ so.

H
An _____ is an important subject that people are arguing about or discussing.

Agents will raise the _____ of prize-money for next year's world championships.
A key _____ for higher education in the 1990's is the need for greater diversity of courses.

B
If you write a _____ to someone, you write a message on paper and send it to them, usually by post.

Our long courtship had been conducted mostly by _____ .

F
If you _____ someone to an event or place, you invite them to go there.

Couldn't you _____ Jon to the party?

Home and Family: 1

A

Last night they stayed at home and watched TV.
... the allocation of land for new homes.

Someone's **home** is the house or flat where they _____ .

B

There's room in there for a family of five.
His family are completely behind him, whatever he decides.

A **family** is a group of people who are related to each other, especially parents and their _____ .

C

I love looking after the children.

If you **look after** someone or something, you do what is necessary to keep them healthy, _____ , or in good condition.

D

She sat on the edge of her mother's bed.
She's an English teacher and a mother of two children.

Your **mother** is the _____ who gave birth to you. You can also call someone your **mother** if she brings you up as if she was this woman.

E

Janine is an only child.
He had grown up an only child in Pittsburgh.

An **only** child is a child who has no _____ or sisters.

F

My family home is in Yorkshire and they don't want to move.
She had often considered moving to London.
The London Evening Standard moved offices a few years ago.

If a person or company **moves**, they _____ the building where they have been living or working, and they go to live or work in a different place, taking their possessions with them.

G

He shared a pizza with his son Laurence.
They have a son.

Someone's **son** is their male _____ .

H

I tried to get in touch with you yesterday evening, but I think you were out.

If you are **out**, you are not at _____ or not at your usual place of work.

Home and Family: 1

D

Your _____ is the woman who gave birth to you. You can also call someone your _____ if she brings you up as if she was this woman.

_____ and child form a close attachment.

G

Someone's _____ is their male child.

Sam is the seven-year-old _____ of Eric Davies.

E

An _____ child is a child who has no brothers or sisters.

'Have you got brothers and sisters?'—'No. I'm an _____ child.'

A

Someone's _____ is the house or flat where they live.

The General divided his time between his shabby offices in Carlton Gardens and his _____ in Hampstead.

C

If you _____ someone or something, you do what is necessary to keep them healthy, safe, or in good condition.

People don't _____ other people's property in the same way as they _____ their own.

H

If you are _____ , you are not at home or not at your usual place of work.

She had to go _____ .

B

A _____ is a group of people who are related to each other, especially parents and their children.

To him the _____ is the core of society.
Does he have any _____ ?

F

If a person or company _____ , they leave the building where they have been living or working, and they go to live or work in a different place, taking their possessions with them.

... when a client changes car or _____ house.

Everyday Situations: 3

A

Accommodation is free – all you pay for is breakfast and dinner.
She paid £300,000 for the 34-room mansion.

When you **pay** an amount of money to someone, you give it to them because you are _____ something from them or because you owe it to them. When you **pay** something such as a bill or a debt, you pay the amount that you owe.

B

I'm hoping you'll keep your promise to come for a long visit.

When you **keep** something such as a promise or an appointment, you do what you _____ you would do.

C

The government is spending billions of dollars on new urban rail projects.

The **dollar** is the unit of money used in the _____, Canada, and some other countries. It is represented by the symbol $. A dollar is divided into one hundred smaller units called cents.

D

Leaphorn put the photograph on the desk.
She hesitated, then put her hand on Grace's arm.

When you **put** something in a particular place or position, you _____ it into that place or position.

E

I received your letter of November 7.

When you **receive** something, you _____ it after someone gives it to you or sends it to you.

F

... a three-course dinner.

A **course** is one part of a _____ .

G

We went on long bicycle rides together.
He and I worked together on a book.

If people do something **together**, they do it with each _____ .

H

Stop throwing those stones!
I've been told to lose weight and stop smoking.
She stopped in mid-sentence.

If you have been doing something and then you **stop** doing it, you no _____ do it.

Everyday Situations: 3

D   When you _____ something in a particular place or position, you move it into that place or position.

Mishka _____ down a heavy shopping bag.

G   If people do something _____ , they do it with each other.

They all live _____ in a three-bedroom house.
_____ they swam to the ship.

E   When you _____ something, you get it after someone gives it to you or sends it to you.

They will _____ their awards at a ceremony in Stockholm.

A   When you _____ an amount of money to someone, you give it to them because you are buying something from them or because you owe it to them. When you _____ something such as a bill or a debt, you _____ the amount that you owe.

He proposes that businesses should _____ taxes to the federal government.
You can _____ by credit card.

C   The _____ is the unit of money used in the USA, Canada, and some other countries. It is represented by the symbol $. A _____ is divided into one hundred smaller units called cents.

He handed her a fifty-_____ bill.

H   If you have been doing something and then you _____ doing it, you no longer do it.

He can't _____ thinking about it.
Does either of the parties want to _____ the fighting?

B   When you _____ something such as a promise or an appointment, you do what you said you would do.

He had again failed to _____ his word.

F   A _____ is one part of a meal.

The lunch was excellent, especially the first _____ .

Talking about People: 2

A

... a young Lithuanian woman named Dayva.
... men and women over 75 years old.

A **woman** is an adult female _____ being.

B

Oh, Amy, I love you.

If you **love** someone, you feel romantically or sexually _____ to them, and they are very important to you.

C

She could, if she wanted, compel him, through a court of law, to support the child after it was born.

You use **it** to refer to a child or baby _____ sex you do not know or _____ sex is not relevant to what you are saying.

D

Walking, done in the right way, is a form of aerobic exercise.
They have computerized systems to ensure delivery of the right pizza to the right place.

If you do something in the **right** way or in the **right** place, you do it as or where it _____ be done or was planned to be done.

E

... Ms Brown.
... Ms Elizabeth Harman.

Ms is used, especially in written English, before a woman's _____ when you are speaking to her or referring to her. If you use **Ms**, you are not specifying if the woman is married or not.

F

I'm not strong enough to carry him.

Someone who is **strong** is healthy with good muscles and can move or carry heavy things, or do hard physical _____ .

G

... a white-haired old man.

Someone who is **old** has lived for many _____ and is no longer young.

H

Losing a game would cause him to fly into a rage.

If you **fly into** a rage or a panic, you suddenly become very _____ or anxious and show this in your behaviour.

Talking about People: 2

D   If you do something in the _ _____ way or in the _____ place, you do it as or where it should be done or was planned to be done.

The chocolate is then melted down to exactly the _____ temperature.
To make sure I did everything _____ , I bought a fat instruction book.

G   Someone who is _____ has lived for many years and is no longer young.

He was considered too _____ for the job.

E   _____ is used, especially in written English, before a woman's name when you are speaking to her or referring to her. If you use _____ , you are not specifying if the woman is married or not.

... _____ Catherine Buckham.

A   A _____ is an adult female human being.

... a _____ doctor.

C   You use _____ to refer to a child or baby whose sex you do not know or whose sex is not relevant to what you are saying.

He threw the baby high in the air and _____ stopped crying.

H   If you _____ a rage or a panic, you suddenly become very angry or anxious and show this in your behaviour.

He was usually a happy and good-tempered child, but on occasions he would _____ a violent rage.

B   If you _____ someone, you feel romantically or sexually attracted to them, and they are very important to you.

We _____ each other. We want to spend our lives together.

F   Someone who is _____ is healthy with good muscles and can move or carry heavy things, or do hard physical work.

I feared I wouldn't be able to control such a _____ horse.

Things We Say: 2

A

I think life itself is a learning process.
The involvement of the foreign ministers was itself a sign of progress.

You use **itself** to _____ the thing you are referring to.

B

Can you just lift the table for a second?
I'm just going to ask you a bit more about your father's business.

You use **just** with instructions, polite requests or statements of intention, to make your request or statement seem _____ difficult and problematical than someone might think.

C

He's generous and, you know, very nice, very polite.

In spoken English, people use **you know** when they are uncertain about what they are saying or what they are going to say _____. Some speakers of English do not like this use.

D

You needn't come again, if you don't want to.

You use **needn't** when you are giving someone _____ not to do something.

E

Come on now. You know you must be hungry.
Come and sit down here, now.

In spoken English, you use **now** to _____ a slight emphasis to a request or command.

F

Of course there were lots of other interesting things at the exhibition.
'I have read about you in the newspapers of course,' Charlie said.

You say **of course** to suggest that something is normal, obvious, or well-known, and should therefore not _____ the person you are talking to.

G

I could call the local doctor.
You could look for a career abroad where environmental jobs are better paid and more secure.
It would be a good idea if you could do this exercise twice or three times on separate days.

You use **could**, or **couldn't** in questions, when you are making offers and _____ .

H

Tell Richard I'm going to kill him when I get hold of him.

If you say that you will **kill** someone for something they have done, you are emphasizing that you are extremely _____ with them.

Things We Say: 2

D You use _____ when you are giving someone permission not to do something.

Well, you _____ tell me anything if you don't want to.

G You use _____ , or _____ in questions, when you are making offers and suggestions.

We need money right? We _____ go around and ask if people need odd jobs done or something.
'It's boring to walk all alone.'—'_____ you go for walks with your friends?'

E In spoken English, you use _____ to give a slight emphasis to a request or command.

_____ don't talk so loud and bother him, honey.

A You use _____ to emphasize the thing you are referring to.

He cheered up on Christmas Day _____ .

C In spoken English, people use _____ when they are uncertain about what they are saying or what they are going to say next. Some speakers of English do not like this use.

I thought I'd, _____ , have a chat with you.

H If you say that you will _____ someone for something they have done, you are emphasizing that you are extremely angry with them.

I'll _____ you if you do that again.

B You use _____ with instructions, polite requests or statements of intention, to make your request or statement seem less difficult and problematical than someone might think.

_____ add water, milk and butter.
I'd _____ like to mention that, personally, I don't think it's wise.
_____ wait for me in the lounge.

F You say _____ to suggest that something is normal, obvious, or well-known, and should therefore not surprise the person you are talking to.

The only honest answer is, _____ , yes.

Time: 2

A
He kissed her again.
Again there was a short silence.

You use **again** to indicate that something happens a _____ time, or after it has already happened before.

B
I had a letter from my mother last week.
This has been on my mind all week.

A **week** is a period of seven _____ . Some people consider that a week starts on Monday and ends on Sunday.

C
Lung cells die and are replaced about once a week.

You use **once** with 'a' and words like 'day', 'week', and 'month' to indicate that something happens regularly, _____ time in each day, week, or month.

D
In the most recent attack one man was shot dead and two others were wounded.

A **recent** event or period of time happened only a _____ while ago.

E
This year's event will take place on June 19th, a week earlier than usual.
She travels to Korea on Monday.
I was born on Christmas day.

You can indicate when something happens by saying that it happens **on** a particular _____ or date.

F
Autumn's my favourite season.
... the rainy season.

The **seasons** are the main periods into which a _____ can be divided and which each have their own typical weather conditions.

G
Blake emigrated to Australia with his family at 13.

If you do something **at** a particular age, you do it _____ you are that age.

H
After 19 May, strikes were occurring on a daily basis.
After breakfast Amy ordered the local taxi to take her to the station.

If something happens **after** a particular date or event, it happens during the period of time that _____ it.

Time: 2

D A _____ event or period of time happened only a short while ago.

Sales have fallen by more than 75 percent in _____ years.

G If you do something _____ a particular age, you do it when you are that age.

Mary Martin has died at her home in California _____ the age of seventy-six.

E You can indicate when something happens by saying that it happens _____ a particular day or date.

I took some photos with her camera _____ my birthday.
Dr. Keen arrived about seven _____ Sunday morning.

A You use _____ to indicate that something happens a second time, or after it has already happened before.

I don't ever want to go through anything like that _____ .

C You use _____ with 'a' and words like 'day', 'week', and 'month' to indicate that something happens regularly, one time in each day, week, or month.

We arranged a special social event _____ a year to which we invited our major customers.

H If something happens _____ a particular date or event, it happens during the period of time that follows it.

It wasn't until _____ Christmas that I met Paul.

B A _____ is a period of seven days. Some people consider that a _____ starts on Monday and ends on Sunday.

I know a wonderful restaurant where we can have lunch next _____ .

F The _____ are the main periods into which a year can be divided and which each have their own typical weather conditions.

... the only region of Brazil where all four _____ are clearly defined.

Essential Words: 3

A

He stood up and began to move around the room.
Snow began falling again.

When someone or something **begins** to do something, they _____ doing it.

B

We waited and waited for news of him.
They still haven't had any news about when they'll be able to go home.

News is _____ about a recently changed situation or a recent event.

C

Economist Jeffrey Faux says a tax cut is a bad idea.
Of course politicians will sometimes make bad decisions.

A **bad** _____, decision, or method is not sensible or not correct.

D

I'm getting a bike for my birthday.
He gets a lot of letters from women.

If you **get** something, you _____ it or are given it.

E

He looks like Father Christmas.
It's a bit like going to the dentist; it's never as bad as you fear.

If you say that one person or thing is **like** another, you mean that the two people or things are _____ or share some of the same qualities, features, or characteristics.

F

People said we were interfering with nature, and that we should just let the animals die.
Thorne let him talk.

If you **let** something happen, you _____ it to happen without doing anything to stop or prevent it.

G

... a council workman who expects to lose his job in the next few weeks.
The talks are expected to continue until tomorrow.
Few expected that he would declare his candidacy for the Democratic nomination for the presidency.
It is expected that the new owner will change the yacht's name.

If you **expect** something to happen, you _____ that it will happen.

H

The meeting quickly ended and Steve and I left the room.
She began to weep. That ended our discussion.

When a situation, process, or activity **ends**, or when something or someone **ends** it, it _____ its final point and stops.

Essential Words: 3

D If you _____ something, you receive it or are given it.

They _____ a salary of $11,000 a year

G If you _____ something to happen, you believe that it will happen.

They no longer _____ corporate profits to improve.
They _____ a gradual improvement in sales of new cars.

E If you say that one person or thing is _____ another, you mean that the two people or things are similar or share some of the same qualities, features, or characteristics.

It's nothing _____ what happened in the mid-Seventies.
This is just _____ old times.
... a mountain shaped _____ a reclining woman.

A When someone or something _____ to do something, they start doing it.

Fry the onion, stirring, until it _____ to soften and brown.

C A _____ idea, decision, or method is not sensible or not correct.

That's not a _____ way to proceed, just somewhat different.

H When a situation, process, or activity _____ , or when something or someone _____ it, it reaches its final point and stops.

They accept that they'll be here until the war _____ .

B _____ is information about a recently changed situation or a recent event.

I wish I had better _____ for you.
He's thrilled to bits at the _____ .

F If you _____ something happen, you allow it to happen without doing anything to stop or prevent it.

She _____ the door slam.
I can't _____ myself be distracted by those things.

Study and Education

A

He went to Hull University, where he studied History and Economics.

If you **study**, you spend time _____ about a particular subject or subjects.

B

... the Faculty of Arts.

At a university or college, **arts** are _____ such as history, literature, or languages in contrast to scientific _____ .

C

... a boy who was in my class at school.
Even the good students say homework is what they most dislike about school.
I took the kids for a picnic in the park after school.

A **school** is a place where _____ are educated. You usually refer to this place as **school** when you are talking about the time that _____ spend there and the activities that they do there.

D

Out of a total of 2,602 pupils only 922 passed the test.

A **test** is a series of questions that you must answer or actions that you must perform in order to show how much you _____ about a subject or how _____ you are able to do something.

E

He was shy and nervous as a boy, and unhappy at school.
It was at university that he first encountered Hopkins.

If someone is **at** school or college, or **at** a particular school or college, they _____ there regularly to study.

F

Claire showed us how to make a chocolate roulade.
Dr. Reichert has shown us a new way to look at those behavior problems.

If you **show** someone how to do something, you do it yourself so that they can _____ you and learn how to do it.

G

Kate's exam results were excellent.

Your **results** are the marks or grades that you _____ for examinations you have taken; used mainly in British English. The usual American term is **scores**.

H

... his researches into which kinds of flowers bees get their best honey from.
... cancer research.

Research is work that involves _____ something and trying to discover facts about it.

Study and Education

D

A _____ is a series of questions that you must answer or actions that you must perform in order to show how much you know about a subject or how well you are able to do something.

She had sold her bike, taken a driving _____ and bought a car.

G

Your _____ are the marks or grades that you get for examinations you have taken; used mainly in British English. The usual American term is _____ .

The Department of Education and Science analysed exam _____ of about 70,000 university graduates.

E

If someone is _____ school or college, or _____ a particular school or college, they go there regularly to study.

I majored in psychology _____ Hunter College.

A

If you _____ , you spend time learning about a particular subject or subjects.

She came to Britain to _____ for her A levels.

C

A _____ is a place where children are educated. You usually refer to this place as _____ when you are talking about the time that children spend there and the activities that they do there.

... a _____ built in the Sixties.
He favors extending the _____ day and _____ year.
... two boys wearing _____ uniform.

H

_____ is work that involves studying something and trying to discover facts about it.

65 percent of the 1987 budget went for nuclear weapons _____ and production.

B

At a university or college, _____ are subjects such as history, literature, or languages in contrast to scientific subjects.

... _____ and social science graduates.

F

If you _____ someone how to do something, you do it yourself so that they can watch you and learn how to do it.

There are seasoned professionals who can teach you and _____ you what to do.
Mother asked me to _____ you how the phones work.

Places and Positions: 2

A

Well, I can't stand here chatting all day.
... the growing number of skiers that come here.
Sheila was in here a minute ago.

You use **here** when you are referring to the _____ where you are.

B

60 years ago half the French population still lived in rural areas.
... mountainous areas of Europe, Asia, North and South America.

An **area** is a particular part of a town, a _____ , a region, or the world.

C

Ahead of you on the right will be a lovely garden.
He looks to his left, up at the screen, then to his right.

The **right** is one of two opposite directions, sides, or positions. If you are facing north and you turn to the right, you will be facing _____ . In the word 'to', the 'o' is to the right of the 't'.

D

... in Frankfurt, where a quarter of the population is foreign.
She was on her first foreign holiday without her parents.
... a foreign language.

Something or someone that is **foreign** comes from or relates to a country that is not your _____ .

E

We had dinner at a restaurant in Attleborough.
He will be at the airport to meet her.

You use **at** to indicate the place or event where something _____ or is situated.

F

... a house, with a high wall all around it.
Mount Marcy is the highest mountain in the Adirondacks.

Something that is **high** extends a long way from the bottom to the _____ when it is upright. You do not use the word **high** to describe people, animals, or plants.

G

Grace sighed so heavily that Trish could hear it in the next room.
The man in the next chair was asleep.

The **next** place or person is the one that is _____ to you or that is the first one that you come to.

H

... the city of Bologna.

A **city** is a large _____ .

Places and Positions: 2

D

Something or someone that is _____ comes from or relates to a country that is not your own.

It is the largest ever private _____ investment in the Bolivian mining sector.

G

The _____ place or person is the one that is nearest to you or that is the first one that you come to.

Stop at the _____ corner. I'm getting out.

E

You use _____ to indicate the place or event where something happens or is situated.

I didn't like being alone _____ home.
Mr Hurd was speaking _____ a news conference in Jordan.

A

You use _____ when you are referring to the place where you are.

I'm not going to stay _____ .
When Mommy comes, just tell her I'm up _____ .

C

The _____ is one of two opposite directions, sides, or positions. If you are facing north and you turn to the _____ , you will be facing east. In the word 'to', the 'o' is to the _____ of the 't'.

Turn _____ into the street.

H

A _____ is a large town.

... a busy _____ centre.

B

An _____ is a particular part of a town, a country, a region, or the world.

... the large number of community groups in the _____ .

F

Something that is _____ extends a long way from the bottom to the top when it is upright. You do not use the word _____ to describe people, animals, or plants.

The gate was too _____ for a man of his age to climb.

Society: 2

A
... the New York Public Library.
The new museum must be accessible by public transport.

Public buildings and services are provided for _____ to use.

B
He spent part of the war in the National Guard.
... matters of war and peace.

A **war** is a period of _____ or conflict between countries or states.

C
... a thirty-two-page pamphlet explaining the rules of basketball.
Sikhs were expected to adhere strictly to the religious rules concerning appearance.
... the amendment to Rule 22.

Rules are instructions that tell you what you are _____ to do and what you are not _____ to do.

D
... the Chorlton Conservative Club.
... a youth club.

A **club** is an organization of people interested in a particular activity or subject who usually _____ on a regular basis.

E
... a member of the Labour party.
... India's ruling party.
... opposition parties.

A **party** is a political organization whose members have similar aims and beliefs. Usually the organization tries to get its members elected to the _____ of a country.

F
Why do you think we should have a vote on that?

A **vote** is an occasion when a group of people make a _____ by each person indicating his or her choice. The choice that most people support is accepted by the group.

G
Such policies would require unprecedented cooperation between nations.
The Arab nations agreed to meet in Baghdad.

A **nation** is an individual _____ considered together with its social and political structures.

H
... President Mubarak.

The **president** of a country that has no king or queen is the person who has the _____ political position and is the leader of the country.

Society: 2

D   A _____ is an organization of people interested in a particular activity or subject who usually meet on a regular basis,

He was _____ secretary.

G   A _____ is an individual country considered together with its social and political structures.

Bill Clinton said that the United States was the only _____ capable of leading the world.

E   A _____ is a political organization whose members have similar aims and beliefs. Usually the organization tries to get its members elected to the government of a country.

... her resignation as _____ leader.

A   _____ buildings and services are provided for everyone to use.

... a _____ health service available to all.

C   _____ are instructions that tell you what you are allowed to do and what you are not allowed to do.

Strictly speaking, this was against the _____ .

H   The _____ of a country that has no king or queen is the person who has the highest political position and is the leader of the country.

The White House says the _____ would veto the bill.

B   A _____ is a period of fighting or conflict between countries or states.

They've been at _____ for the last fifteen years.

F   A _____ is an occasion when a group of people make a decision by each person indicating his or her choice. The choice that most people support is accepted by the group.

They took a _____ and decided not to do it.

Grammar Words: 3

A

I could run faster than everyone else my age.
There was no way she could have coped with a baby around.

You use **could** to indicate that someone _____ the ability to do something. You use **could not** or **couldn't** to say that someone _____ unable to do something.

B

The communique gave no other details.

You use **other** to refer to an additional thing or person of the _____ type as one that has been mentioned or is known about.

C

When Ann arrived home that night, she found Brian in the house watching T.V.
She was seventeen and she had no education or employment.

You use **she** to refer to a _____ , girl, or female animal who has already been mentioned or whose identity is clear.

D

The process is not a circle but rather a spiral.
But there must be no talk of final victory; rather, the long, hard slog to a solution.

You use **rather** when you are making a _____ with what you have just said, especially when you are describing the true situation after saying what it is not.

E

I never went through a final exam that was as difficult as that one.
There was no obvious reason why this could not be as good a film as the original.

You use the structure **as ... as** when you are _____ things.

F

The tug crossed our stern not fifty yards away.
. . . a large crowd not ten yards away waiting for a bus.

You can use **not** in front of a word referring to a distance, length of time, or other amount to say that the actual distance, time, or amount is _____ than the one mentioned.

G

I still dream of home.
Brian's toe is still badly swollen and he cannot put on his shoe.

If a situation that used to exist **still** exists, it has continued and exists _____ .

H

Brian splashed water on his face, then brushed his teeth.

You use **his** to indicate that something belongs or relates to a man, _____ , or male animal.

55

Grammar Words: 3

D　You use _____ when you are making a contrast with what you have just said, especially when you are describing the true situation after saying what it is not.

Twenty million years ago, Idaho was not the arid place it is now. _____ , it was warm and damp, populated by dense primordial forest.

G　If a situation that used to exist _____ exists, it has continued and exists now.

If you don't like the job, why are you _____ there?

E　You use the structure _____ ... _____ when you are comparing things.

Being a mother isn't _____ bad _____ I thought at first!
I don't think he was ever _____ fit _____ he should have been.

A　You use _____ to indicate that someone had the ability to do something. You use _____ or _____ to say that someone was unable to do something.

For my return journey, I felt I _____ afford the extra and travel first class.
When I left school at 16, I _____ read or write.

C　You use _____ to refer to a woman, girl, or female animal who has already been mentioned or whose identity is clear.

_____ was a little fluffy baby duck which we reared until _____ was fully grown.

H　You use _____ to indicate that something belongs or relates to a man, boy, or male animal.

The past 10 years have been the happiest and most fulfilling of _____ life.

B　You use _____ to refer to an additional thing or person of the same type as one that has been mentioned or is known about.

They were just like any _____ young couple.
Four crewmen were killed, one _____ was injured.

F　You can use _____ in front of a word referring to a distance, length of time, or other amount to say that the actual distance, time, or amount is less than the one mentioned.

They were here _____ five minutes ago!

Everyday Situations: 4

A

He secretly tried to block her advancement in the Party.
I tried calling him when I got here but he wasn't at home.
No matter how bad you feel, keep trying.

If you **try** to do something, you want to do it, and you _____
action which you hope will help you to do it.

B

Ray will earn his keep on local farms while studying.

Someone's **keep** is the _____ of food and other things that they
need in their daily life.

C

Enjoy your food.
... frozen foods.

Food is what people and animals _____ .

D

Your old clothes will be gratefully accepted by jumble sale organisers.
All those invited to next week's peace conference have accepted.

If you **accept** something that you have been offered, you say
_____ to it or agree to take it.

E

They can now be bought fresh in supermarkets.
Lizzie bought herself a mountain bike.

If you **buy** something, you obtain it by paying _____ for it.

F

Hobart found it difficult to get her first book published.
The lack of childcare provisions made it difficult for single mothers to get jobs.
It was a very difficult decision to make.

Something that is **difficult** is not _____ to do, understand, or
deal with.

G

She heard no further sounds.
The trumpet can be heard all over their house.
They heard the protesters shout: 'No more fascism!'
And then we heard the bells ringing out.

When you **hear** a _____ , you become aware of it through your
ears.

H

The Croatian authorities closed the airport.
The restaurant was closed for the night.

When a shop or other public place **closes** or **is closed**, work or activity
_____ there for a short period, for example during the night or
at lunchtime.

Everyday Situations: 4

D

If you _____ something that you have been offered, you say yes to it or agree to take it.

Eventually Stella persuaded her to _____ an offer of marriage.

G

When you _____ a sound, you become aware of it through your ears.

It's nice to _____ the church bells ring

E

If you _____ something, you obtain it by paying money for it.

He could not afford to _____ a house.
I'd like to _____ him lunch.

A

If you _____ to do something, you want to do it, and you take action which you hope will help you to do it.

_____ to make the effort to work your way through all of your tasks one at a time.
Does it annoy you if others do things less well than you would, or don't seem to _____ hard enough?
It wasn't that she'd really expected to get any money out of him; it had just seemed worth a _____ .

C

_____ is what people and animals eat.

... supplies of _____ and water.
... emergency _____ aid.

H

When a shop or other public place _____ or is _____ , work or activity stops there for a short period, for example during the night or at lunchtime.

Shops _____ only on Christmas Day and New Year's Day.
This was Saturday, the bank was _____ for the weekend.

B

Someone's _____ is the cost of food and other things that they need in their daily life.

I need to give my parents money for my _____ .

F

Something that is _____ is not easy to do, understand, or deal with.

We're living in _____ times.
It's very _____ being a woman in motor racing.

Entertainment and Leisure

A

There has been a lively interest in the elections in the last two weeks.
His parents tried to discourage his interest in music, but he persisted.

If you have an **interest** in something, you want to learn or hear
_____ about it.

B

They played in the little garden.
Polly was playing with her teddy bear.

When _____ , animals, or perhaps adults **play**, they spend time
doing enjoyable things, such as using toys and taking part in games.

C

The team failed to qualify for the African Nations Cup finals.

A **team** is a group of people who play a particular sport or game
together _____ other similar groups of people.

D

... the midweek international against England.

In sport, an **international** is a match that is played between teams
representing two different _____ ; used mainly in British
English.

E

The couple met at a party.
Most teenagers like to go to parties.

A **party** is a social event, often in someone's _____ , at which
people enjoy themselves doing things such as eating, drinking,
dancing, talking, or playing games.

F

... classical music.
... the music of George Gershwin.

Music is the pattern of _____ produced by people singing or
playing instruments.

G

He was watching a football match.

A **match** is an organized game of football, tennis, cricket, or other
_____ ; used mainly in British English.

H

The second story in the book is titled 'The Scholar'.
I shall tell you a story about four little rabbits.

A **story** is a description of imaginary people and events, which is
written or _____ in order to entertain.

Entertainment and Leisure

D   In sport, an _____ is a match that is played between teams representing two different countries; used mainly in British English.

He played in an _____ for Poland.

G   A _____ is an organized game of football, tennis, cricket, or other sport; used mainly in British English.

France won the _____ 28-19.

E   A _____ is a social event, often in someone's home, at which people enjoy themselves doing things such as eating, drinking, dancing, talking, or playing games.

We threw a huge birthday _____ .

A   If you have an _____ in something, you want to learn or hear more about it.

She'd liked him at first, but soon lost _____ .
Food was of no _____ to her at all.

C   A _____ is a group of people who play a particular sport or game together against other similar groups of people.

He had lost his place in the England _____ .

H   A _____ is a description of imaginary people and events, which is written or told in order to entertain.

... a popular love _____ with a happy ending.

B   When children, animals, or perhaps adults _____ , they spend time doing enjoyable things, such as using toys and taking part in games.

We could invite the children round to _____ .
... a few hours of _____ until the baby-sitter takes them off to bed.

F   _____ is the pattern of sounds produced by people singing or playing instruments.

... a mixture of _____ , dance, cabaret and children's theatre.
... a _____ critic for the New York Times.

Numbers: 2

A

She lost 16 pounds in the first month of her diet.
... the first few flakes of snow.

The **first** thing, person, event, or period of time is the one that happens or comes _____ all the others of the same kind.

B

It would be very nice if we had a true figure of how many people in this country haven't got a job.
New Government figures predict that one in two marriages will end in divorce.

A **figure** is a particular amount expressed as a _____ , especially a statistic.

C

Stephanie and David redecorated a room in just three days.

You use **just** to draw attention to how _____ an amount is or how short a length of time is.

D

He visited me twice that fall and called me on the telephone often.
The government has twice declined to back the scheme.
Thoroughly brush teeth and gums twice daily.

If something happens **twice**, there are _____ actions or events of the same kind.

E

I don't think many people would argue with that.
Not many films are made in Finland.
Do you keep many books and papers and memorabilia?

You use **many** to indicate that you are talking about a _____ number of people or things.

F

He is adding three aircraft carriers – that makes six in all.

You can use **make** to say what two numbers _____ up to.

G

People should eat less fat to reduce the risk of heart disease.
... a dishwasher that uses less water and electricity than older machines.

You use **less** to indicate that there is a _____ number of things or a _____ amount of something than before or than average, or than something else.

H

The students work in groups on complex problems.

A **group** of people or things is a number of people or things that are _____ in one _____ at one time.

61

Numbers: 2

D   If something happens _____ , there are two actions or events of the same kind.

_____ before he had been in New York with Gladys on summer vacations.

G   You use _____ to indicate that there is a smaller number of things or a smaller amount of something than before or than average, or than something else.

Children of very low ability should not be permitted to pay _____ attention to the sciences.

E   You use _____ to indicate that you are talking about a large number of people or things.

_____ holidaymakers had avoided the worst of the delays by consulting tourist offices.
Acting is definitely a young person's profession in _____ ways.

A   The _____ thing, person, event, or period of time is the one that happens or comes before all the others of the same kind.

Two years ago Johnson came _____ in the one hundred metres at Seoul.
The second paragraph startled me even more than the _____ .

C   You use _____ to draw attention to how small an amount is or how short a length of time is.

Remember he's _____ fourteen years old.

H   A _____ of people or things is a number of people or things that are together in one place at one time.

The trouble involved a small _____ of football supporters.

B   A _____ is a particular amount expressed as a number, especially a statistic.

It will not be long before the inflation _____ starts to fall.

F   You can use _____ to say what two numbers add up to.

Four twos _____ eight.

Things We Say: 3

A

'More wine?'—'Yes please.'
'Will you take me there?'—'Yes, I will.'

You use **yes** to accept an _____ or request, or to give permission.

B

It was law or classics – I mean English or classics.

You say **I mean** when correcting something that you have _____ said.

C

I'd like the use of your living room, if I may.
May I come with you to Southampton?

You use **may** when you are making polite _____ .

D

Excuse me sir, but would you mind telling me what sort of car that is?

People sometimes say **sir** as a very formal and polite way of addressing a _____ whose name they do not know or a _____ of superior rank. For example, a shop assistant might address a male customer as **sir**.

E

It's an old trick but it just might work.

You use **just** with 'might,' 'may,' and 'could', when you mean that there is a _____ chance of something happening, despite the fact that it is not very likely.

F

The neglect that large cities like New York have received over the past 12 years is tremendous.

You can use **like** to introduce an _____ of the set of things or people that you have just mentioned.

G

Would you like a drink?
Would you like to stay?

You use **would**, usually in questions, when you are politely _____ someone something or inviting someone to do something.

H

The formula in Hollywood is simple – money talks.

If you say that **money talks**, you mean that if someone has a lot of money, they also have a lot of _____ .

Things We Say: 3

D People sometimes say _____ as a very formal and polite way of addressing a man whose name they do not know or a man of superior rank. For example, a shop assistant might address a male customer as _____ .

Good afternoon to you, _____ .

G You use _____ , usually in questions, when you are politely offering someone something or inviting someone to do something.

Perhaps you _____ like to pay a visit to London.

E You use _____ with 'might,' 'may,' and 'could', when you mean that there is a small chance of something happening, despite the fact that it is not very likely.

It may _____ be possible.

A You use _____ to accept an offer or request, or to give permission.

'Can I ask you something?'—'_____ , of course.'

C You use _____ when you are making polite requests.

Ah, Julia, my dear, here is our guest. _____ we have some tea?

H If you say that _____ , you mean that if someone has a lot of money, they also have a lot of power.

If someone sees birds that are not for sale and still wants them, _____ .

B You say _____ when correcting something that you have just said.

She will go up the stairs and into the Pavilion, sorry _____ the Cathedral.

F You can use _____ to introduce an example of the set of things or people that you have just mentioned.

He could say things _____ , 'Let's go to the car' or 'Let us go for a walk' in French.

Time: 3

A

I've just bought a new house.
The two had only just met and were barely friends.

You use **just** to say that something happened a very _____ time ago, or is starting to happen at the present time. For example, if you say that someone has **just** arrived, you mean that they arrived a very _____ time ago.

B

The pizza will then take about twenty minutes to cook.
Bye mum, see you in a minute.
Within minutes we realized our mistake.

A **minute** is one of the sixty parts that an _____ is divided into. You can also use **minute** in a more general way to mean a short length of time.

C

She left yesterday.
In yesterday's games, Switzerland beat the United States two-one.

You use **yesterday** to refer to the day before _____ .

D

He took one last quick look about the room.
I just popped in for a quick drink.
My father would have driven me to Cornwall, but we decided it would be quicker by train.

Something that is **quick** takes or lasts only a _____ time.

E

Next, close your eyes then screw them up tight.
I don't know what to do next.

The thing that happens **next** is the thing that happens immediately _____ something else.

F

She said if the world did not act conclusively now, it would only bequeath the problem to future generations.
The domestic debate on Denmark's future role in Europe rages on.

Future things will happen or exist after the _____ time.

G

For a few minutes she sat on her bed watching the clock.
He smoked one and a half packs of cigarettes a day for about 25 years.

You use **for** to say how long something _____ or continues.

H

Over the next several months I met most of her family.
They had all spent £180 for a month's unlimited train travel around Europe.

A **month** is a period of about _____ weeks.

Time: 3

D   Something that is _____ takes or lasts only a short time.

Although this recipe looks long, it is actually very _____ to prepare.

G   You use _____ to say how long something lasts or continues.

The toaster remained on _____ more than an hour.
They talked _____ a bit.

E   The thing that happens _____ is the thing that happens immediately after something else.

The news is _____ .

A   You use _____ to say that something happened a very short time ago, or is starting to happen at the present time. For example, if you say that someone has _____ arrived, you mean that they arrived a very short time ago.

I _____ had the most awful dream.
I'm only _____ beginning to take it in that he's still missing.

C   You use _____ to refer to the day before today.

_____ she announced that she is quitting her job.

H   A _____ is a period of about four weeks.

She was here for a _____ .

B   A _____ is one of the sixty parts that an hour is divided into. You can also use _____ in a more general way to mean a short length of time.

Half a _____ later she came in the front door.

F   _____ things will happen or exist after the present time.

... the _____ King and Queen.

Essential Words: 4

A

She could have made the sandwich herself; her mum needn't have bothered to do anything.
I was a little nervous when I announced my engagement to Grace, but I needn't have worried.

If someone **needn't** have done something, it was not _____ or useful for them to do it, although they did it.

B

I know that you led a rifle platoon during the Second World War.
'How did he meet your mother?'—'I don't know.'

If you **know** a fact, a _____ of information, or an answer, you have it correctly in your mind.

C

She is small for her age.
The window was far too small for him to get through.

A **small** person, _____, or amount of something is not large in physical size.

D

The electoral council announced that all eligible people would get a chance to vote.
Most refugee doctors never get the chance to practise medicine in British hospitals.

If you have a **chance** to do something, you have the _____ to do it.

E

I love sweets but Mum doesn't let me have them very often.
The Americans won't let her leave the country.

If you **let** someone do something, you give them your _____ to do it.

F

London was different from most European capitals.
If he'd attended music school, how might things have been different?

If two people or things are **different**, they are not _____ each other or not the same as each other.

G

I had an idea that he joined the army later, after university, but I may be wrong.

If you have an **idea** that something is the case, you think that it _____ be the case, although you are not certain.

H

I can't think why Grace doesn't like me.
What music do you like best?

If you **like** something or someone, you _____ them interesting, enjoyable, or attractive.

Essential Words: 4

D If you have a _____ to do something, you have the opportunity to do it.

I felt I had to give him a _____ .

G If you have an _____ that something is the case, you think that it may be the case, although you are not certain.

I have an _____ that some of the boys upstate are up to their old tricks.

E If you _____ someone do something, you give them your permission to do it.

Visa or no visa, they won't _____ you into the country.

A If someone _____ have done something, it was not necessary or useful for them to do it, although they did it.

We spent a hell of a lot of money that we _____ have spent.

C A _____ person, thing, or amount of something is not large in physical size.

Next door to the garage is a _____ orchard area.
Stick them on using a _____ amount of glue.

H If you _____ something or someone, you find them interesting, enjoyable, or attractive.

I just didn't _____ being in crowds.
Do you _____ to go swimming?
I _____ my whisky neat.

B If you _____ a fact, a piece of information, or an answer, you have it correctly in your mind.

'People like doing things for nothing.'—'I _____ they do.'
I don't _____ what happened to her husband.
We all _____ about his early experiments in flying.

F If two people or things are _____ , they are not like each other or not the same as each other.

We have totally _____ views.

Talking about People: 3

A

... the human body.
... human history.

Human means relating to or concerning _____ .

B

The maid looked at him, a nervous smile on her face.

If someone has a particular expression **on** their _____ , their
_____ has that expression.

C

Things weren't so bad, after all. I was among friends again.

If you are **among** people of a particular kind, you are _____
them and having contact _____ them.

D

Sheila was looking miserable.
I shall use the money to make my home look lovely.
You don't look 15 years old.

You use **look** when describing the _____ of a person or thing or
the impression that they give.

E

*I was sitting on the floor shivering with fear because a bullet had been
fired through a window.*
... boyhood memories of sickness and fear of the dark.

Fear is the unpleasant feeling you have when you think that you are
in _____ .

F

... Mr Grant.
... Mr Bob Price.

Mr is used before a _____ name when you are speaking or
referring to him.

G

Phil was now much more independent of his parents.
She would like to be financially independent.

If someone is **independent**, they are _____ to live as they want,
because they do not need help and have no obligations to anyone.

H

She was the last to go to bed.

If you are the **last** to do or know something, everyone else does or
knows it _____ you.

Talking about People: 3

D You use _____ when describing the appearance of a person or thing or the impression that they give.

He does not _____ the most reliable of animals.
They _____ like stars to the naked eye.

G If someone is _____ , they are free to live as they want, because they do not need help and have no obligations to anyone.

There were benefits to being a single _____ woman.

E _____ is the unpleasant feeling you have when you think that you are in danger.

London Zoo is running hypnosis programmes to help people overcome their _____ of spiders.

A _____ means relating to or concerning people.

The _____ body accepts a lot of abuse: tobacco, alcohol, bad diet, lack of exercise.

C If you are _____ people of a particular kind, you are with them and having contact with them.

I was brought up _____ people who read and wrote a lot.

H If you are the _____ to do or know something, everyone else does or knows it before you.

Riccardo and I are always the _____ to know what's going on.

B If someone has a particular expression _____ their face, their face has that expression.

She looked at him with a hurt expression _____ her face.

F _____ is used before a man's name when you are speaking or referring to him.

... _____ and Mrs Daniels.

Communication: 3

A

'How is Frank?' he asked.
I wasn't the only one asking questions.
She asked me if I'd enjoyed my dinner.

If you **ask** someone something, you say something to them in the form of a question because you want to know the _____ .

B

... a piece of paper.
She sat at the table with pen and paper.

Paper is a material that you _____ on or wrap things with. The pages of this book are made of paper.

C

He doesn't speak English.

If you **speak** a _____ language, you know the language and are able to have a conversation in it.

D

I read about it in the paper.

When you **read** something such as a book or article, you look at and _____ the words that are written there.

E

... the letters of the alphabet.

Letters are written symbols which represent one of the _____ in a language.

F

... a man claiming to be a journalist.
'I had never received one single complaint against me,' claimed the humiliated doctor.

If you say that someone **claims** that something is true, you mean they say that it is true but you are not sure _____ or not they are telling the truth.

G

She broke down describing how she was arrested for refusing a breath test.
She read a poem by Carver which describes their life together.
Just before his death he described seeing their son in a beautiful garden.

If you **describe** a person, object, event, or situation, you say _____ they are _____ or what happened.

H

I was earning a lot of money, but that was not the issue.
She avoided the issue by ordering a turkey sandwich.

If something is **the issue**, it is the thing you consider to be the most _____ part of a situation or discussion.

Communication: 3

D When you _____ something such as a book or article, you look at and understand the words that are written there.

It was nice to _____ that the Duke will not be sending his son off to boarding school.

G If you _____ a person, object, event, or situation, you say what they are like or what happened.

We asked her to _____ what kind of things she did in her spare time.

E _____ are written symbols which represent one of the sounds in a language.

... the _____ E.

A If you _____ someone something, you say something to them in the form of a question because you want to know the answer.

You will have to _____ David about that.
'I'm afraid to _____ what it cost.'—'Then don't _____ .'

C If you _____ a foreign language, you know the language and are able to have a conversation in it.

Many of them can _____ two or three or more languages.

H If something is the _____ , it is the thing you consider to be the most important part of a situation or discussion.

Do not draw it on the chart, however, as this will confuse the _____ .
The real _____ was never addressed.

B _____ is a material that you write on or wrap things with. The pages of this book are made of _____ .

... a sheet of pretty wrapping _____ .
... a _____ bag.

F If you say that someone _____ that something is true, you mean they say that it is true but you are not sure whether or not they are telling the truth.

He _____ a 70 to 80 per cent success rate.

Talking about Things: 2

A
Once the container is full, it stays shut until you turn it clockwise.

If something is **full**, it contains as much of a substance or as many objects as it _____ .

B
... one of the main tourist areas of Amsterdam.
My main concern now is to protect the children.

The **main** thing is the most _____ one of several similar things in a particular situation.

C
... a bunch of red roses.

Something that is **red** is the _____ of blood or of a ripe tomato.

D
All it required was a bit of work.

A **bit** of something is a _____ amount of it.

E
She loved the big old house.
These books must be very old.
... an old Arab proverb.

Something that is **old** has existed for a _____ time.

F
The houses were all the same – square, close to the street, needing paint.
In essence, all computers are the same.
People with the same experience in the job should be paid the same.
Driving a boat is not the same as driving a car.

If two or more things, actions, or qualities are the **same**, or if one is the **same** as another, the two are very similar or exactly _____ each other in some way.

G
Crime is an increasingly serious problem in Russian society.
The government still face very serious difficulties.

Serious problems or situations are very _____ and cause people to be worried or afraid.

H
... her deep brown eyes.

Something that is **brown** is the colour of earth, or of the bark of a _____ .

73

Talking about Things: 2

D A _____ of something is a small amount of it.

I got paid a little _____ of money.

G _____ problems or situations are very bad and cause people to be worried or afraid.

Doctors said his condition was _____ but stable.

E Something that is _____ has existed for a long time.

... her _____ habit of criticizing his speech.
Ethnic tensions are an _____ problem here.

A If something is _____ , it contains as much of a substance or as many objects as it can.

... a _____ tank of petrol.

C Something that is _____ is the colour of blood or of a ripe tomato.

She had small hands with nails painted bright _____ .

H Something that is _____ is the colour of earth, or of the bark of a tree.

... a package wrapped in _____ paper.

B The _____ thing is the most important one of several similar things in a particular situation.

What are the _____ differences and similarities between them?

F If two or more things, actions, or qualities are the _____ , or if one is the _____ as another, the two are very similar or exactly like each other in some way.

I want my son to wear the _____ clothes as everyone else at the school.
Bihar had a population roughly the _____ as that of England.

Everyday Situations: 5

A

When I opened my eyes I saw a man with an axe standing at the end of my bed.

When you **open** your eyes or your eyes **open**, you move your eyelids upwards, for example when you wake up, so that you can _____ .

B

... the small income he had shared with his brother.
Scarce water resources are shared between states.
Most hostel tenants would prefer single to shared rooms.

If you **share** something with another person, you _____ have it, use it, or occupy it. You can also say that two people **share** something.

C

Efforts were made to limit the sale of alcohol.

The **sale** of goods is the act of _____ them for money.

D

He showed me the flat he shares with Esther.
I showed them where the gun was.

If you **show** someone something, you give it to them, take them to it, or point to it, so that they can _____ it or know what you are referring to.

E

He insisted that the conflict would continue until conditions were met for a ceasefire.
... the continued existence of a species.

If something **continues** or if you **continue** it, it does not _____ happening.

F

... cups and saucers.
Mix about four cups of white flour with a pinch of salt.

A **cup** is a small round container that you _____ from. Cups usually have handles and are made from china or plastic.

G

... the only time that we attempted to do something like that.

If you **attempt** to do something, especially something difficult, you _____ to do it.

H

Juventus have spent £23m on new players.
The survey may cost at least £80 but is money well spent.

When you **spend** money, you _____ money for things that you want.

75

Everyday Situations: 5

D If you _____ someone something, you give it to them, take them to it, or point to it, so that they can see it or know what you are referring to.

Cut out this article and _____ it to your bank manager.

G If you _____ to do something, especially something difficult, you try to do it.

Before I could _____ a reply he added over his shoulder: 'Wait there.'

E If something _____ or if you _____ it, it does not stop happening.

Outside the building people _____ their vigil, huddling around bonfires.

A When you _____ your eyes or your eyes _____ , you move your eyelids upwards, for example when you wake up, so that you can see.

As soon as he saw her eyes _____ he sat up.

C The _____ of goods is the act of selling of them for money.

... a proposed arms _____ to Saudi Arabia.

H When you _____ money, you pay money for things that you want.

Businessmen _____ enormous amounts advertising their products.

B If you _____ something with another person, you both have it, use it, or occupy it. You can also say that two people _____ something.

Two Americans will _____ this year's Nobel Prize for Medicine.

F A _____ is a small round container that you drink from. _____ usually have handles and are made from china or plastic.

He sipped his coffee and put his _____ down.

Work: 2

A

Once I'm in America I can get a job.
Thousands have lost their jobs.

A **job** is the _____ that someone does to earn money.

B

His father kept a village shop.

If you **keep** a business such as a small shop or hotel, you _____ it and manage it.

C

The chef at the barbecue looked up from his labours; he was sweating.

Labour is very _____ work, usually physical work.

D

He left school with no qualifications.
I am leaving to concentrate on writing fiction.

If you **leave** an institution, group, or job, you permanently _____ attending that institution, being a member of that group, or doing that job.

E

I feel that women in all types of employment can benefit from joining a union.

A **union** is a workers' organization which represents its members and which aims to improve things such as their working conditions and _____ .

F

My grandfather was secretary of the Scottish Miners' Union.

The **secretary** of an organization such as a trade union, a _____ party, or a club is its official manager.

G

... the acting president, who's standing in while Franco's out of the country.

If you **stand in** for someone, you take their _____ or do their job, because they are ill or away.

H

Like working women anywhere, Asian women are buying convenience foods.

Working people have jobs which they are _____ to do.

77

Work: 2

D If you _____ an institution, group, or job, you permanently stop attending that institution, being a member of that group, or doing that job.

He may just decide to _____ .

G If you _____ for someone, you take their place or do their job, because they are ill or away.

I had to _____ for her on Tuesday when she didn't show up.

E A _____ is a workers' organization which represents its members and which aims to improve things such as their working conditions and pay.

. . . _____ officials.

A A _____ is the work that someone does to earn money.

I felt the pressure of being the first woman in the _____ .
. . . overseas _____ vacancies.

C _____ is very hard work, usually physical work.

. . . the _____ of seeding, planting and harvesting.

H _____ people have jobs which they are paid to do.

The majority of _____ women are in low-paid jobs.

B If you _____ a business such as a small shop or hotel, you own it and manage it.

Mr. Blair used to _____ the village shop down here.

F The _____ of an organization such as a trade union, a political party, or a club is its official manager.

Jack McConnell has been appointed _____ of the Labour party in Scotland.

Grammar Words: 4

A

After lunch Elizabeth and I did the washing up.
Dad does the garden.

Do is often used instead of a more specific verb, to talk about a common action involving a particular thing. For example you can say 'do your teeth' instead of '_____ your teeth'.

B

We're going to have another baby.

Another means _____ more thing or person of the kind mentioned.

C

Janis and Kurt have announced their engagement.
... as the trees shed their leaves and the year begins to die.

You use **their** to indicate that something belongs or relates to the group of people, animals, or _____ that you are talking about.

D

... such careers as teaching, nursing, hairdressing and catering.

You use **such ... as** to introduce one or more _____ of the kind of thing or person that you have just mentioned.

E

I've done nothing much since coffee time.
Mr Pearson said he knew nothing of his wife's daytime habits.

Nothing means not a _____ thing, or not a _____ part of something.

F

'You said you'd stay till tomorrow.'—'I know, Bel, but I think I would rather go back.'
... very hot but not boiling.

You use **but** to introduce something which _____ with what you have just said, or to introduce something which adds to what you have just said.

G

They had already voted for him at the first ballot.
The group has already shed 10,000 jobs.

You use **already** to focus on the fact that something has happened, or that something had happened _____ the moment you are referring to.

H

I'm very sorry. I really am.
It really is best to manage without any medication if you possibly can.

You can use **really** to _____ a statement; used mainly in spoken English.

Grammar Words: 4

D   You use _____ to introduce one or more examples of the kind of thing or person that you have just mentioned.

... delays caused by _____ things _____ bad weather or industrial disputes.

G   You use _____ to focus on the fact that something has happened, or that something had happened before the moment you are referring to.

They've spent nearly a billion dollars on it _____ .

E   _____ means not a single thing, or not a single part of something.

He was dressed in jeans and _____ else.

A   _____ is often used instead of a more specific verb, to talk about a common action involving a particular thing. For example you can say '_____ your teeth' instead of 'brush your teeth'.

I was trying to _____ some work.
Let me _____ your hair.

C   You use _____ to indicate that something belongs or relates to the group of people, animals, or things that you are talking about.

Horses were poking _____ heads over _____ stable doors.

H   You can use _____ to emphasize a statement; used mainly in spoken English.

You know, we _____ ought to get another car.
I'm fine, _____ I'm fine.

B   _____ means one more thing or person of the kind mentioned.

The demand generated by one factory required the construction of _____ .

MPs have one free trip to Brussels and _____ to Strasbourg, headquarters of the EC, each year.

F   You use _____ to introduce something which contrasts with what you have just said, or to introduce something which adds to what you have just said.

He not only wants to be taken seriously as a musician, _____ as a poet too.

Movement and Travel: 2

A

We went to Rome.
Gladys had just gone into the kitchen.
I went home at the weekend.

When you **go** somewhere, you _____ or travel there.

B

The planes flew through the clouds.
The bird flew away.

When something such as a bird, insect, or aircraft **flies**, it moves through the _____ .

C

Newman walked along the street alone.
The young man led Mark Ryle along a corridor.

If you move or look **along** something such as a road, you move or look towards one _____ of it.

D

Our correspondent Stephen Sackur has just returned from the camps on the border.
So far more than 350,000 people have returned home.

When you **return** to a place, you go _____ there after you have been away.

E

Don't try to get on or off a moving train!
As he stepped off the aeroplane, he was shot dead.

When you get **off** a bus, train, or plane, you come out of it or _____ it after you have been travelling on it.

F

He did not stop until he reached the door.
When the bus reached High Holborn, Tony rang the bell and they jumped off together.

When someone or something **reaches** a place, they arrive _____ .

G

An injured policeman was led away by colleagues.
He walked away from his car.
She drove away before either of them could speak again.

If someone or something moves or is moved **away** from a place, they move or are moved so that they are _____ longer there. If you are **away** from a place, you are not in the place where people expect you to be.

H

They'd come on a direct flight from the Soviet Union.
... the direct route from Amman to Bombay.

Direct means moving _____ a place or object, without changing direction and without stopping, for example in a journey.

Movement and Travel: 2

D When you _____ to a place, you go back there after you have been away.

There are unconfirmed reports that Aziz will _____ to Moscow within hours.

G If someone or something moves or is moved _____ from a place, they move or are moved so that they are no longer there. If you are _____ from a place, you are not in the place where people expect you to be.

Jason was _____ on a business trip.
Simon had been _____ a good deal lately.

E When you get _____ a bus, train, or plane, you come out of it or leave it after you have been travelling on it.

At the next stop the man got _____ too and introduced himself.

A When you _____ somewhere, you move or travel there.

It took us an hour to _____ three miles.

C If you move or look _____ something such as a road, you move or look towards one end of it.

I looked _____ the length of the building.

H _____ means moving towards a place or object, without changing direction and without stopping, for example in a journey.

You can fly _____ to Amsterdam from most British airports.

B When something such as a bird, insect, or aircraft _____ , it moves through the air.

The eagle _____ highest in the sky.

F When someone or something _____ a place, they arrive there.

When it _____ Mars in August, the spacecraft will enter a highly elliptical orbit.

Places and Positions: 3

A
Good agricultural land is in short supply.
... 160 acres of land.

Land is an _____ of ground, especially one that is used for a particular purpose such as farming or building.

B
She kept her money under the mattress.
She remembered where she kept the gun.

If you **keep** something in a particular place, you always have it or store it in that place so that you can _____ it whenever you need it.

C
In the north the ground becomes very cold as the winter snow and ice covers the ground.

The **north** is the direction which is on your _____ when you are looking towards the direction where the sun rises.

D
Her lips were close to his head and her breath tickled his ear.
The whales were too close; this posed an immediate problem for my photography.
The man moved closer, lowering his voice.

If one thing or person is **close** to another, there is only a very small distance _____ them.

E
He took his feet off the desk.
I took the key for the room off a rack above her head.

If something is taken **off** something else or moves **off** it, it is no _____ touching that thing.

F
They were on the upper floor of the building.

A **building** is a structure that has a roof and _____ , for example a house or a factory.

G
A large wooden table dominates the centre of the room.

The **centre** of something is the _____ of it.

H
We'd better check on the match in the local paper.
Some local residents joined the students' protest.

Local means existing in or belonging to the _____ where you live, or to the _____ that you are talking about.

Places and Positions: 3

D   If one thing or person is _____ to another, there is only a very small distance between them.

The tables were pushed _____ together so diners could talk across the aisles.

G   The _____ of something is the middle of it.

Bake until light golden and crisp around the edges and slightly soft in the _____ .

E   If something is taken _____ something else or moves _____ it, it is no longer touching that thing.

Hugh wiped the rest of the blood _____ his face with his handkerchief.
Lee broke _____ a small piece of orange and held it out to him.

A   _____ is an area of ground, especially one that is used for a particular purpose such as farming or building.

. . . a small piece of grazing _____ .

C   The _____ is the direction which is on your left when you are looking towards the direction where the sun rises.

Birds usually migrate from _____ to south.

H   _____ means existing in or belonging to the area where you live, or to the area that you are talking about.

I was going to pop up to the _____ library.

B   If you _____ something in a particular place, you always have it or store it in that place so that you can use it whenever you need it.

To make it easier to contact us, _____ this card handy.

F   A _____ is a structure that has a roof and walls, for example a house or a factory.

Crowds gathered around the Parliament _____ .

Things We Say: 4

A

'Bring us something to drink.' – 'Yeah, yeah.'

Yeah is used in written English to represent the way '_____' is pronounced in informal speech.

B

Perhaps the most important lesson to be learned is that you simply cannot please everyone.
His very last paintings are perhaps the most puzzling.
The lesson from all of this is perhaps a broader one.

You use **perhaps** in opinions and remarks to make them appear _____ definite or more polite.

C

May we suggest you try one of our guest houses?
May I help you?

You use **may**, usually in questions, when you are politely making suggestions or _____ to do something; a formal use.

D

Now, look, here is how things stand.

You say **look** when you want someone to pay attention to you because you are going to say something _____ .

E

Now then, I think the Queen should be taxed.
Well then, I'll put the kettle on and make us some tea.

You use **then** with words like 'now', 'well', and 'okay', to introduce a new topic or a new _____ of view.

F

Now, erm, obviously some of our listeners may have some ideas.

In informal English, some people say **'Now'** when they are _____ of what to say next.

G

I need to speak with her right this minute.

If you say that something must be done **this minute**, you are emphasizing that it must be done _____ .

H

I am never really happy staying in a hotel, although the management here have been kindness itself.
Many men are charm itself.

If you say that someone is, for example, politeness **itself** or kindness **itself**, you are _____ that they are extremely polite or extremely kind.

Things We Say: 4

D You say _____ when you want someone to pay attention to you because you are going to say something important.

   _____ , I'm sorry. I didn't mean it.

G If you say that something must be done _____ , you are emphasizing that it must be done immediately.

   Anna, stop that. Sit down _____ .

E You use _____ with words like 'now', 'well', and 'okay', to introduce a new topic or a new point of view.

   Okay _____ let me ask how you do that.

A _____ is used in written English to represent the way 'yes' is pronounced in informal speech.

   'Do you know what I mean?'—'_____ .'

C You use _____ , usually in questions, when you are politely making suggestions or offering to do something; a formal use.

   Do sit down. And _____ we offer you something to drink?
   _____ we recommend a weekend in Stockholm?

H If you say that someone is, for example, politeness _____ or kindness _____ , you are emphasizing that they are extremely polite or extremely kind.

   The story is simplicity _____ .

B You use _____ in opinions and remarks to make them appear less definite or more polite.

   Do you _____ disapprove of Agatha Christie and her Poirot and Miss Marple?
   He's not _____ the easiest person to live with.

F In informal English, some people say '_____ ' when they are thinking of what to say next.

   _____ , er, dogs can live to fifteen.

Essential Words: 5

A

We know of the incident but have no further details.
He said he did not know of any specific terrorist threat.

If you say that you **know of** something, you mean that you've
_____ about it but you do not necessarily have a lot of
information about it.

B

Experts say a 'yes' vote is still the likely outcome.
If this is your first baby, it's far more likely that you'll get to the hospital too early.

You use **likely** to indicate that something is _____ the case or
will _____ happen in a particular situation.

C

On their way back to Marseille they spoke very little.

Little means not very often or to only a _____ extent.

D

... an art dealer from Zurich.
Katy Jones is nineteen and comes from Birmingham.

Someone who comes **from** a particular place lives in that place or
originally lived there. Something that comes **from** a particular place
was _____ in that place.

E

You get time to think in prison.

If you **get** the time or opportunity to do something, you _____
the time or opportunity to do it.

F

He was abandoned by his father when he was three months old.
The paintings in the chapel were perhaps a thousand years old.
Bill was six years older than David.

You use **old** to talk or ask about how many days, weeks, months, or
years someone or something has _____ or existed.

G

It was a very severe accident and he lost part of his foot.
Mum and he were able to walk part of the way together.

Part of something is _____ of it.

H

She went and turned the sound down.

The **sound** on a television, radio, or record player is what you
_____ coming from the machine. Its loudness can be controlled.

Essential Words: 5

D Someone who comes _____ a particular place lives in that place or originally lived there. Something that comes _____ a particular place was made in that place.

... wines _____ Coteaux d'Aix-en-Provence.

G _____ something is some of it.

Woodhead spent _____ his childhood in Rhodesia.

E If you _____ the time or opportunity to do something, you have the time or opportunity to do it.

... whenever I _____ the chance I go to Maxim's for dinner.

A If you say that you _____ something, you mean that you've heard about it but you do not necessarily have a lot of information about it.

I _____ a very pleasant inn not far away.

C _____ means not very often or to only a small extent.

Only Africa is at present _____ affected by hard drugs.

H The _____ on a television, radio, or record player is what you hear coming from the machine. Its loudness can be controlled.

Compact discs have brought about a vast improvement in recorded _____ quality.

B You use _____ to indicate that something is probably the case or will probably happen in a particular situation.

Francis thought it _____ John still loved her.
Profit will most _____ have risen by about £25 million.

F You use _____ to talk or ask about how many days, weeks, months, or years someone or something has lived or existed.

How _____ are you now?
These weren't young kids, they were as _____ as I was.

88

Time: 4

A

I knew I had to get up early.
Why do we have to go to bed so early?

Early means _____ the usual time that a particular event or activity happens.

B

We had a long meeting with the attorney general.
She is planning a long holiday in Egypt and America.

A **long** event or period of _____ lasts for a great amount of _____ or takes a great amount of _____ .

C

Let's plan a big night next week.
He retires next January.
Next day the European Community summit strengthened their ultimatum.

You use **next** in expressions such as 'next Friday' and 'next year' to refer, for example, to the Friday or year which follows immediately _____ the present one or _____ the previous one.

D

They arrived at the weekend and gave three concerts in the week.

The week is the part of a seven-day period that does not _____ Saturday and Sunday, when people are usually at work.

E

... the Welsh Boat Show, planned for July 30-August 1.

If something is planned **for** a particular time, it is planned to _____ then.

F

During the morning your guide will take you around the city.
On Sunday morning Bill was woken by the telephone.

The **morning** is the part of each _____ between the time that people usually wake up and noon or lunchtime.

G

We went to bed very late.
He married late.

Late means _____ the usual time that a particular event or activity happens.

H

'What time is it?'—'Eight o'clock.'
He asked me the time.
What time did he leave?

You use **time** to ask or talk about a specific point in the day, which can be stated in _____ and minutes and is shown on clocks.

Time: 4

D

The _____ is the part of a seven-day period that does not include Saturday and Sunday, when people are usually at work.

. . . the hard work of looking after the children during the _____ .

G

_____ means after the usual time that a particular event or activity happens.

They had a _____ lunch in a cafe.
He was a very _____ developer.

E

If something is planned _____ a particular time, it is planned to happen then.

The party was scheduled _____ 7:00.

A

_____ means before the usual time that a particular event or activity happens.

I decided that I was going to take _____ retirement.
I planned an _____ night.

C

You use _____ in expressions such as '_____ Friday' and '_____ year' to refer, for example, to the Friday or year which follows immediately after the present one or after the previous one.

He predicted that the region's economy would grow by about six per cent both this year and _____ .

H

You use _____ to ask or talk about a specific point in the day, which can be stated in hours and minutes and is shown on clocks.

I phoned my mother to ask what _____ she was coming home.
The _____ is now 19 minutes past the hour.

B

A _____ event or period of time lasts for a great amount of time or takes a great amount of time.

They sat looking at each other for a _____ while.
He must have started writing his book a _____ time ago.

F

The _____ is the part of each day between the time that people usually wake up and noon or lunchtime.

He read about it in his _____ paper.

Body and Health: 2

A   *He spent the last fourteen years of his life in retirement.*

Someone's **life** is the period of _____ during which they are alive.

B   *She stamped her foot again.*
... a foot injury.

Your **feet** are the parts of your body that are at the ends of your _____ , and that you stand on.

C   *I had a headache.*
He might be having a heart attack.
She has epilepsy.

If you **have** an illness or disability, you _____ from it.

D   *Johnson cut himself shaving.*
I started to cry because I cut my finger.
He had sustained a cut on his left eyebrow.

If you **cut** yourself or **cut** a part of your body, you accidentally injure yourself on a _____ object so that you bleed.

E   *She turned her head away from him.*

Your **head** is the _____ part of your body, which has your eyes, mouth, and brain in it.

F   *The official number of people carrying the AIDS virus is low.*

If a person or animal **is carrying** a disease, they are infected with it and can _____ it on to other people or animals.

G   *Severe shock can bring on an attack of acne.*
Bob died of a heart attack, brought on by his lifestyle.

If something **brings on** an illness, pain, or feeling, especially one that you often suffer from, it _____ you to have it.

H   *More than 1,000 people have been killed by the armed forces.*
Cattle should be killed cleanly and humanely.
The earthquake killed 62 people.
Heroin can kill.

If a person, animal, or other living thing **is killed**, something or someone causes them to _____ .

Body and Health: 2

D   If you _____ yourself or _____ a part of your body, you accidentally injure yourself on a sharp object so that you bleed.

Zoe was badly _____ as she scrambled down rocks to reach him.
Blood from his _____ lip trickled over his chin.
All I got was assorted _____ and bruises.

G   If something _____ an illness, pain, or feeling, especially one that you often suffer from, it causes you to have it.

His research has demonstrated that traffic pollution in cities _____ attacks of hay fever.

E   Your _____ is the top part of your body, which has your eyes, mouth, and brain in it.

He took a puff on his pipe and shook his _____ .

A   Someone's _____ is the period of time during which they are alive.

For the first time in his _____ he regretted that he had no faith.

C   If you _____ an illness or disability, you suffer from it.

People who _____ diabetes are more likely to develop heart disease than people who don't _____ diabetes.

H   If a person, animal, or other living thing is _____ , something or someone causes them to die.

In the story a young history teacher is _____ .

B   Your _____ are the parts of your body that are at the ends of your legs, and that you stand on.

... his aching arms and sore _____ .

F   If a person or animal is _____ a disease, they are infected with it and can pass it on to other people or animals.

Frogs eat pests which destroy crops and _____ diseases.

Everyday Situations: 6

A

He had plenty of work to do.

If you **have** something to do, you are responsible for doing it or _____ do it.

B

Peter offered to teach them water-skiing.
'Can I get you a drink,' she offered.

If you **offer** to do something, you say that you are _____ to do it.

C

The seminars are free, with lunch provided.

If something is **free**, you can have it or use it without _____ for it.

D

The waitress had cleared away the plates and brought coffee.
Tania cooked, served, and cleared away.

When you **clear** things **away** or you **clear away**, you put away the things that you have been _____ , especially for eating or cooking.

E

The police also found a pistol.
They have spent ages looking at the map and can't find a trace of anywhere called Darrowby.

If you **find** someone or something, you _____ them or learn where they are.

F

She handed the knife back.
Put it back in the freezer.

If you give or put something **back**, you _____ it to the person who had it or to the place where it was before you took it. If you get or take something **back**, you then have it again after not having it for a while.

G

I resolved not to waste money on a hotel.
He spent more on feeding the dog than he spent on feeding himself.

When you buy something or pay for something, you _____ money **on** it.

H

Don't worry, Xiao, I won't let you down.
When such advisers fail in their duty, they let down the whole system.

If you **let** someone **down** you disappoint them, by not doing something that you have said you will do or that they _____ you to do.

Everyday Situations: 6

D When you _____ things _____ or you _____ _____ , you put away the things that you have been using, especially for eating or cooking.

_____ *that stuff _____ will you, Jim?*
I was helping Mrs. Blount _____ _____ the things from the table.

G When you buy something or pay for something, you spend money _____ it.

More money should be spent _____ education and housing.

E If you _____ someone or something, you see them or learn where they are.

I wonder if you could _____ me a deck of cards?

A If you _____ something to do, you are responsible for doing it or must do it.

I _____ some important calls to make.

C If something is _____ , you can have it or use it without paying for it.

... a _____ brochure with details of gift vouchers.

H If you _____ someone _____ you disappoint them, by not doing something that you have said you will do or that they expected you to do.

The company now has a large number of workers who feel badly _____ _____ .

B If you _____ to do something, you say that you are willing to do it.

I was hoping he would _____ to take me home.

F If you give or put something _____ , you return it to the person who had it or to the place where it was before you took it. If you get or take something _____ , you then have it again after not having it for a while.

You'll get your money _____ .

Movement and Travel: 3

A   *She's going tomorrow.*

When you **go**, you _____ the place where you are.

B   *His daughter Carly drove him to the train station.*

If you **drive** someone somewhere, you _____ them there in a car or other vehicle.

C   *David had been dancing about like a child, but suddenly he stood still and looked at Brad.*
He played the tape through once, then sat very still for several minutes.

If you stay **still**, you stay in the same position and do not _____ .

D   *Remember to bring an apron or an old shirt to protect your clothes.*

If you **bring** someone or something _____ you when you come to a place, they come _____ you or you have them _____ you.

E   *I have no idea how he got into Iraq.*
She got up and went into an inner office.

If you go **into** a place or vehicle, you move from being outside it to being _____ it.

F   *There was very little traffic on the roads.*
We just go straight up the Bristol Road.
He was coming down the road the same time as the girl was turning into the lane.

A **road** is a long piece of hard ground which is built between two _____ so that people can drive or ride easily from one _____ to the other.

G   *It was dark by the time she got home.*

When you **get** to a place, you _____ there.

H   *I went back to bed.*
Mr Mandela is due back in South Africa today.
Smith changed his mind and moved back home.

If someone or something goes **back** somewhere, they _____ to the place where they were before.

Movement and Travel: 3

D If you _____ someone or something with you when you come to a place, they come with you or you have them with you.

Mum wants me to _____ home a copy of the match programme.

G When you _____ to a place, you arrive there.

Generally I _____ to work at 9.30am.

E If you go _____ a place or vehicle, you move from being outside it to being inside it.

He got _____ bed and started to read.

A When you _____ , you leave the place where you are.

Let's _____ .

C If you stay _____ , you stay in the same position and do not move.

He recalled her _____ face and the hurt in her eyes when he had refused her help.
Gladys was _____ , then she shook her head slowly.

H If someone or something goes _____ somewhere, they return to the place where they were before.

I'll be _____ as soon as I can.
He made a round-trip to the terminal and _____ .

B If you _____ someone somewhere, you take them there in a car or other vehicle.

Let me _____ Miss Jones back to Thomas Street.

F A _____ is a long piece of hard ground which is built between two places so that people can drive or ride easily from one place to the other.

Buses carry 30 per cent of those travelling by _____ .
You mustn't lay all the blame for _____ accidents on young people.

Home and Family: 2

A *She has moved to a small house and is living off her meagre savings.*

A **house** is a _____ in which people live, usually the people belonging to one family.

B *The bedroom walls would be papered with chintz.*
She checked the wall clock.

A **wall** is one of the vertical sides of a building or _____ .

C *His father was a painter.*
He would be a good father to my children.

Your **father** is the _____ who made your mother pregnant with you. You can also call someone your **father** if he brings you up as if he was this man.

D *Ted's always been difficult, Mr Kemp – he takes after his dad.*

If you **take after** a member of your family, you resemble them in your _____ , your behaviour, or your character.

E *She has lived here for 10 years.*
He still lives with his parents.

If someone **lives** in a particular place or with a particular person, their _____ is in that place or with that person.

F *Is it difficult being a single mother?*

Someone who is **single** is_____ married. You can also use **single** to describe someone who does _____ have a girlfriend or boyfriend.

G *His sister Sarah helped him.*
... Vanessa Bell, the sister of Virginia Woolf.

Your **sister** is a _____ or woman who has the same parents as you.

H *She grew up in Tokyo.*

When someone **grows up**, they gradually change from being a _____ into being an adult.

Home and Family: 2

D If you _____ a member of your family, you resemble them in your appearance, your behaviour, or your character.

The children love parties. They must _____ their mother.

G Your _____ is a girl or woman who has the same parents as you.

I didn't know you had a _____ .

E If someone _____ in a particular place or with a particular person, their home is in that place or with that person.

She always said I ought to _____ alone.
Where do you _____ ?

A A _____ is a building in which people live, usually the people belonging to one family.

... her parents' _____ in Warwickshire.

C Your _____ is the man who made your mother pregnant with you. You can also call someone your _____ if he brings you up as if he was this man.

... Mr Stoneman, a _____ of five.

H When someone _____ , they gradually change from being a child into being an adult.

What does Marylin want to do when she _____ ?

B A _____ is one of the vertical sides of a building or room.

Kathryn leaned against the _____ of the church.

F Someone who is _____ is not married. You can also use _____ to describe someone who does not have a girlfriend or boyfriend.

I now have to face the rest of my life as a _____ person.

Talking about People: 4

A
At least one person died and several others were injured.
Everyone knows he's the only person who can do the job.

A **person** is a _____ , a woman, or a child.

B
He was a big man, smartly dressed in a suit and tie.
... three women in black.

If you are dressed **in** a piece of clothing, you are _____ it.

C
She has a nephew who is just ten years of age.
At the age of sixteen he qualified for a place at the University of Hamburg.

Your **age** is the number of _____ that you have lived.

D
All the Indian batsmen played well.
He speaks English better than I do.

If you do something **well**, you do it to a _____ standard or to a great extent.

E
He worked for the rights of black people.
Sherry is black, tall, slender and soft-spoken.

A **black** person belongs to a race of people with _____ skins, especially a race from Africa.

F
She and Linda became very close.
As a little girl, Karan was closest to her sister Gail.

You say that people are **close** to each other when they _____ each other very much and know each other very well.

G
You are good to me.
Her good intentions were thwarted almost immediately.

Someone who is **good** is _____ and thoughtful.

H
He has a large, generous face with deep lines.

The **lines** on someone's skin, especially on their face, are long thin marks that appear there as they grow _____ .

Talking about People: 4

D   If you do something _____ , you do it to a high standard or to a great extent.

It is a formula that worked very _____ indeed.
I don't really know her very _____ .

G   Someone who is _____ is kind and thoughtful.

Just ask the Admiral if he will be _____ enough to drop me a note.

E   A _____ person belongs to a race of people with dark skins, especially a race from Africa.

... the traditions of the _____ community.

A   A _____ is a man, a woman, or a child.

My great-grandfather was a _____ of some importance here.
The amount of sleep we need varies from _____ to _____ .

C   Your _____ is the number of years that you have lived.

I admired him for being so confident at his _____ .

H   The _____ on someone's skin, especially on their face, are long thin marks that appear there as they grow older.

... fine _____ and wrinkles.

B   If you are dressed _____ a piece of clothing, you are wearing it.

... an American lady _____ a gray sweater and pink skirt.

F   You say that people are _____ to each other when they like each other very much and know each other very well.

I shared a house with a _____ friend from school.
I had a _____ relationship with my grandfather.

Society: 3

A

He's well liked by people in the community.
'The community are getting impatient,' said a representative of the Residents' Association.

The **community** is all the people who _____ in a particular area or place.

B

No-one enjoys paying tax.
... a pledge not to raise taxes.

Tax is an amount of _____ that you have to pay to the government so that it can pay for public services.

C

They formed themselves into teams.

If an organization, group, or company **is formed**, it _____ into existence.

D

They are seeking permission to begin criminal proceedings against him for breaking the law on financing political parties.
There must be changes in the law quickly to stop this sort of thing ever happening to anyone else.

The **law** is a system of _____ that a society or government develops in order to deal with crime, business agreements, and social relationships.

E

... a fully independent state.

Independent countries and states are not ruled by other countries but have their own _____ .

F

After returning from France, he joined the army.
The army is about to launch a major offensive.

An **army** is a large organized group of people who are armed and trained to fight on land in a _____ . Most armies are organized and controlled by governments.

G

All other political parties there have been completely banned.
The Canadian government is facing another political crisis.

Political means relating to the way _____ is achieved and used in a country or society.

H

Leaders of the Southern states are meeting in Louisville.

Some large _____ such as the USA are divided into smaller areas called **states**.

Society: 3

D The _____ is a system of rules that a society or government develops in order to deal with crime, business agreements, and social relationships.

Obscene and threatening phone calls are against the _____ .

G _____ means relating to the way power is achieved and used in a country or society.

... a democratic _____ system.

E _____ countries and states are not ruled by other countries but have their own government.

Papua New Guinea became _____ from Australia in 1975.

A The _____ is all the people who live in a particular area or place.

The growth of such vigilante gangs has worried _____ leaders, police and politicians.

C If an organization, group, or company is _____ , it comes into existence.

The African Children's Choir was _____ in 1984.

H Some large countries such as the USA are divided into smaller areas called _____ .

... experimental job creation programmes run not by the federal government but by individual _____ .

B _____ is an amount of money that you have to pay to the government so that it can pay for public services.

... a cut in _____ on new cars.
His decision to return to a form of property _____ is the right one.

F An _____ is a large organized group of people who are armed and trained to fight on land in a war. Most _____ are organized and controlled by governments.

... a top-ranking _____ officer.

Grammar Words: 5

A

I don't like sitting in an office.

Don't is the usual spoken form of _____ .

B

I never make any big decisions.
We are doing this all without any support from the hospital.

You use **any** in statements with negative meaning to indicate that _____ thing or person of a particular type exists, is present, or is involved in a situation.

C

What you wear should be stylish and clean, and must definitely fit well.
The doctor must not allow the patient to be put at risk.

You use **must** to indicate that you think it is very important or _____ for something to happen. You use **must not** or **mustn't** to indicate that you think it is very important or _____ for something not to happen.

D

I went in the room and told her I had something to say to her.

You use **her** to refer to a woman, _____ , or female animal.

E

I made a few phone calls.
I think you're making a serious mistake.
The Pope said the world had made some progress towards peace.
She had made us an offer too good to refuse.

You can use **make** with a wide range of nouns to indicate that someone performs an action or says something. For example, if someone **makes** a suggestion, they _____ something.

F

Only the President could authorize the use of the atomic bomb.
Only here were the police visible in any strength at all.

You use **only** to state the _____ thing that is true, appropriate, or necessary in a particular situation, in contrast to all the other things that are not true, appropriate, or necessary.

G

Jacques Arnold has been a member of parliament since 1987.
She had a sort of breakdown some years ago, and since then she has been very shy.

You use **since** when you are mentioning a time or event in the past and indicating that a situation has _____ from then until now.

H

Jim and I are getting married.

A speaker or writer uses **I** to refer to _____ or herself. **I** is a first person singular pronoun. **I** is used as the subject of a verb.

Grammar Words: 5

D   You use _____ to refer to a woman, girl, or female animal.

Catherine could not give _____ the advice she most needed.

G   You use _____ when you are mentioning a time or event in the past and indicating that a situation has continued from then until now.

I've been here _____ the end of June.
When we first met, we had a row, and we have rowed frequently ever _____ .

E   You can use _____ with a wide range of nouns to indicate that someone performs an action or says something. For example, if someone _____ a suggestion, they suggest something.

I'd just like to _____ a comment.

A   _____ is the usual spoken form of 'do not'.

I _____ want to live here.

C   You use _____ to indicate that you think it is very important or necessary for something to happen. You use _____ or _____ to indicate that you think it is very important or necessary for something not to happen.

You are going to have to take a certain amount of criticism, but you _____ cope with it.
We _____ forget your birthday.

H   A speaker or writer uses _____ to refer to himself or herself. _____ is a first person singular pronoun. _____ is used as the subject of a verb.

She liked me, _____ think.

B   You use _____ in statements with negative meaning to indicate that no thing or person of a particular type exists, is present, or is involved in a situation.

I'm not making _____ promises.

F   You use _____ to state the one thing that is true, appropriate, or necessary in a particular situation, in contrast to all the other things that are not true, appropriate, or necessary.

44-year-old woman seeks caring, honest male of similar age for friendship and fun. Genuine replies _____ .
A business can _____ be built and expanded on a sound financial base.

Essential Words: 6

A

If it is possible to find out where you brother is, we shall.
Everything is possible if we want it enough.
It's been a beautiful evening and you have made it all possible.

If it is **possible** to do something, it _____ be done.

B

The building needs quite a few repairs.
... a garden that needs tidying.

If an object or place **needs** something doing to it, that action must or
should be done to _____ the object or place, or to _____ a
situation. If a task **needs** doing, it must or should be done to
_____ a situation.

C

*He'd never been in a class before and he was not even sure that he
should have been teaching.*
*The president has never been sure which direction he wanted to go in
on this issue.*

If you are **sure** that something is true, you are _____ that it is
true. If you are not **sure** about something, you do not know for
certain what the true situation is.

D

The expression on his face changed from sympathy to surprise.
Unemployment has fallen from 7.5 to 7.2%.

If something changes **from** one thing to another, it stops being the
first thing and _____ the second thing.

E

It sounds like a wonderful idea to me, does it really work?
It sounds as if they might have made a dreadful mistake.

When you are describing your impression or opinion of something
you have _____ about or read about, you can talk about the
way it **sounds**.

F

The thought of Nick made her throat tighten.
I tormented myself with the thought that life was just too comfortable.

A **thought** is an _____ that you have in your mind.

G

His father owns a local pub.

If you **own** something, it is your _____ .

H

*It is the work of Ivor Roberts-Jones, who also produced the statue of
Churchill in Parliament Square.*
He is an asthmatic who was also anaemic three months ago.

You can use **also** to give more _____ about a person or thing, or
to add another relevant fact.

Essential Words: 6

D   If something changes _____ one thing to another, it stops being the first thing and becomes the second thing.

I made a switch _____ butter to olive oil for much of my cooking.

G   If you _____ something, it is your property.

Do you _____ a car?

E   When you are describing your impression or opinion of something you have heard about or read about, you can talk about the way it _____ .

The book is not as morbid as it _____ .
I know this _____ a crazy thing for me to ask you.

A   If it is _____ to do something, it can be done.

This morning he had tried every way _____ to contact her.
Live as you like, leave home if you want – that was never _____ when I was young.

C   If you are _____ that something is true, you are certain that it is true. If you are not _____ about something, you do not know for certain what the true situation is.

She was no longer _____ how she felt about him.
It is impossible to be _____ about the value of land.

H   You can use _____ to give more information about a person or thing, or to add another relevant fact.

She has a reputation for brilliance. _____ , she is gorgeous.

B   If an object or place _____ something doing to it, that action must or should be done to improve the object or place, or to improve a situation. If a task _____ doing, it must or should be done to improve a situation.

The taste of vitamins is not too nice so the flavour sometimes _____ to be disguised.

F   A _____ is an idea that you have in your mind.

He pushed the _____ from his mind.
I've just had a _____ .

Communication: 4

A

She read through pages and pages of the music I had brought her.
I only had time to skim through the script before I flew over here.

If you read **through** something, you read it from beginning to
_____ .

B

Where's your book? Take it out and turn to page 4.
. . . 1,400 pages of top-secret information.

A **page** is one side of one of the pieces of _____ in a book,
magazine, or newspaper. Each page usually has a number printed at
the top or bottom.

C

A passer-by told the driver to move his car so that it was not causing an
obstruction.
She told me on the telephone to come help clean the house.

If you **tell** someone to do something, you _____ or advise them
to do it.

D

They asked a great many questions about England.
The President refused to answer further questions on the subject.

A **question** is something which you say or write in order to
_____ someone about something.

E

Hey, Terry, come and meet my Dad.

If you **meet** someone, you are introduced to them and begin talking
to them and getting to _____ them.

F

I'm not making it up. The character exists in real life.

If you **make up** something such as a _____ or excuse, you
invent it, sometimes in order to deceive people.

G

The growing problem is underlined in the latest issue of the Lancet.

An **issue** of something such as a magazine or newspaper is the
version of it that is published, for example, in a particular month or
on a particular _____ .

H

Would you call me as soon as you find out? My number's in the phone
book.
'May I speak with Mr Coyne, please?'—'May I ask who's calling?'

If you **call** someone, you _____ them.

Communication: 4

D
A _____ is something which you say or write in order to ask someone about something.

Right, next _____ .

'Do you feel that the British gamble more than they should?'—'Well, that's a very difficult _____ to answer.'

G
An _____ of something such as a magazine or newspaper is the version of it that is published, for example, in a particular month or on a particular day.

I read Germaine Greer's article in the March _____ with particular interest.

E
If you _____ someone, you are introduced to them and begin talking to them and getting to know them.

In her new life, the young girl began to _____ new people.

A
If you read _____ something, you read it from beginning to end.

The article had been authored by Raymond Kennedy. He read it straight _____ , looking for any scrap of information that might have passed him by.

C
If you _____ someone to do something, you order or advise them to do it.

I had to _____ him to get out.

H
If you _____ someone, you telephone them.

A friend of mine gave me this number to _____ .

B
A _____ is one side of one of the pieces of paper in a book, magazine, or newspaper. Each _____ usually has a number printed at the top or bottom.

... the front _____ of the Guardian.

F
If you _____ something such as a story or excuse, you invent it, sometimes in order to deceive people.

I think it's very unkind of you to _____ stories about him.

Everyday Situations: 7

A

The assistant carried on talking.
His eldest son Joseph carried on his father's traditions.

If you **carry on** doing something, you _____ to do it.

B

He laughed with pleasure when people said he looked like his dad.
The British don't laugh at the same jokes as the French.
'They'll carry me away on a stretcher if I win on Sunday,' laughed Lyle.

When you **laugh**, you make a sound with your throat while smiling and show that you are _____ or amused. People also sometimes laugh when they feel nervous or are being unfriendly.

C

He sold boots on a market stall.

A **market** is a place where goods are _____ and _____ , usually in the open air.

D

The Workers' Party failed to win a single governorship.
He failed in his attempt to take control of the company.
Many of us have tried to lose weight and failed miserably.

If you **fail** to do something that you were trying to do, you are unable to do it or do not _____ in doing it.

E

You do have to consider the feelings of those around you.
Consider how much you can afford to pay for a course, and what is your upper limit.

If you **consider** something, you think _____ it carefully.

F

It's healthy to eat when I'm hungry and to stop when I'm full.

If you feel **full**, you have eaten or drunk so much that you do not _____ anything else.

G

Trim off the excess pastry using a sharp knife.
He had simply used a little imagination.
Officials used loud hailers to call for calm.

If you **use** something, you do something with it in order to do a job or to achieve a particular _____ or effect.

H

He died two and a half years later, leaving everything to his wife.

If you **leave** property or money to someone, you arrange for it to be given to them after you have _____ .

Everyday Situations: 7

D If you _____ to do something that you were trying to do, you are unable to do it or do not succeed in doing it.

Dixon says doctors sometimes _____ to diagnose the onset of Aids.

G If you _____ something, you do something with it in order to do a job or to achieve a particular result or effect.

_____ a vegetable knife to cut and scrape the asparagus tips.

E If you _____ something, you think about it carefully.

The government is being asked to _____ a plan to fix the date of the Easter break.

A If you _____ doing something, you continue to do it.

Rachael Carr intends to _____ teaching.
Her bravery has given him the will to _____ with his life and his work.

C A _____ is a place where goods are bought and sold, usually in the open air.

For local flavour try a morning at the street _____ in Castries.

H If you _____ property or money to someone, you arrange for it to be given to them after you have died.

She told me she had changed her mind and she wanted to _____ the house to you.

B When you _____ , you make a sound with your throat while smiling and show that you are happy or amused. People also sometimes _____ when they feel nervous or are being unfriendly.

He was about to offer an explanation, but she was beginning to _____ .

Lysenko gave a deep rumbling _____ at his own joke.

F If you feel _____ , you have eaten or drunk so much that you do not want anything else.

Most fast foods are low in fibre, which means you need to eat a lot to feel _____ .

Wordlist 1

The following list comprises the 664 most frequent words in the English language, based on the evidence of The Bank of English. In the *COBUILD English Dictionary* and the *COBUILD Learner's Dictionary*, the entries for these words are marked with five black diamonds (♦♦♦♦♦). All the items in this book are adapted from the entries for these words in the *COBUILD English Dictionary*, so you can use this list to help you find all the words you need to fill in the gaps on the *right*-hand pages (and on many of the left-hand pages as well). Note that only the simplest form of each word is given here; you may need a different form of the word, or more than one word, to fill in the gaps correctly.

a	anything	blue
able	appear	body
about	area	book
accept	arm	both
accord	army	boy
according to	around	break
account	art	bring
across	as	brother
act	ask	brown
action	at	build
actually	attack	building
add	attempt	business
after	authority	but
again	available	buy
against	away	by
age	back	call
ago	bad	campaign
agree	bank	can
aid	base	capital
air	based	car
all	be	care
allow	beat	carry
almost	because	case
along	become	cause
already	before	central
also	begin	centre
although	behind	century
always	believe	chance
among	better	change
an	between	charge
and	big	chief
announce	billion	child
another	bit	city
answer	bite	claim
any	black	class

clear	down	find
close	draw	firm
club	drive	first
colour	drug	five
come	during	fly
coming	each	follow
committee	early	food
common	east	foot
community	easy	for
company	economic	force
complete	economy	foreign
concern	education	form
condition	effect	former
conference	effort	forty
consider	eight	four
continue	eighteen	fourteen
control	eighty	free
cost	either	friend
could	election	from
council	eleven	front
country	else	full
course	end	fund
court	enough	further
cover	er	future
create	even	game
cup	event	general
current	ever	get
cut	every	girl
daughter	everything	give
day	example	go
deal	expect	going
decide	experience	good
decision	eye	got
demand	face	government
department	fact	great
describe	fail	green
design	fall	grey
develop	family	ground
development	far	group
didn't	father	grow
die	fear	half
different	feel	hand
difficult	few	happen
direct	fifteen	hard
director	fifty	have
do	fight	he
doesn't	figure	head
dollar	film	health
don't	final	hear
door	financial	help

her	laugh	month
here	law	more
herself	lead	morning
high	leader	most
him	learn	mother
himself	least	move
his	leave	Mr
history	left	Mrs
hit	less	Ms
hold	let	much
home	letter	music
hope	level	must
hospital	life	my
host	like	name
hour	likely	nation
house	line	national
how	list	near
however	little	need
human	live	never
hundred	local	new
idea	long	news
if	look	newscaster
important	lose	next
in	lot	night
include	love	nine
including	low	nineteen
increase	main	ninety
independent	major	no
industry	make	north
information	man	not
interest	many	nothing
international	market	now
into	match	number
issue	matter	of
it	may	of course
its	me	off
itself	mean	offer
job	meet	office
join	meeting	officer
just	member	official
keep	middle	often
kill	might	oh
kind	military	oil
know	million	old
labour	mind	on
land	mine	once
large	minister	one
last	minute	only
late	moment	open
later	money	operate

113

operation
or
order
other
our
out
outside
over
own
page
paper
parent
part
party
pass
past
pay
peace
people
per cent
perhaps
person
photo
place
plan
plant
play
player
point
police
policy
political
position
possible
pound
power
president
press
pressure
price
prime minister
probably
problem
process
produce
product
programme
provide
public
put

question
quick
quite
race
radio
raise
rate
rather
reach
read
real
really
reason
receive
recent
record
red
release
remain
remember
report
research
result
return
right
rise
road
role
room
rule
run
sale
same
save
say
school
season
second
secretary
security
see
seek
seem
sell
send
sense
serious
service
set
seven

seventeen
seventy
several
share
she
short
should
show
side
sign
since
single
sir
sister
sit
situation
six
sixteen
sixty
small
so
social
society
some
something
son
soon
sort
sound
south
speak
special
spend
staff
stage
stand
star
start
state
stay
step
still
stock
stop
story
street
strong
student
study
such

suggest
support
sure
system
take
talk
tax
team
tell
ten
term
test
than
thank
that
the
their
them
themselves
then
there
these
they
thing
think
thirteen
thirty
this
those
though
thought
thousand
three
through
time
to
today

together
too
top
total
towards
town
trade
try
turn
twelve
twenty
twice
two
under
understand
union
university
until
up
us
use
value
very
view
visit
vote
wait
walk
wall
want
war
watch
water
way
we
week
well

west
what
when
where
whether
which
while
white
who
whole
whose
why
wide
wife
will
win
with
within
without
woman
word
work
worker
working
world
would
write
yeah
year
yes
yesterday
yet
you
young
your